DATE DUE

Wankel

Wankel

The Curious Story Behind the Revolutionary Rotary Engine

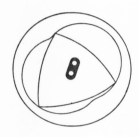

NICHOLAS FAITH

STEIN AND DAY/*Publishers*/New York

First published in 1975
Copyright © 1975 by Nicholas Faith
All rights reserved
Designed by Ed Kaplin
Printed in the United States of America
Stein and Day /*Publishers*/Scarborough House,
Briarcliff Manor, N.Y. 10510

Library of Congress Cataloging in Publication Data

Faith, Nicholas, 1933–
    Wankel.

    Bibliography: p. 239
    Includes index.
    1. Wankel engine.   I.   Title.
TL210.7.F34   621.43′4   74-78521
ISBN 0-8128-1719-2

Acknowledgments

This book covers such large technical, financial, and geographical areas that for much of the information I have had to rely on the efforts of some far-flung correspondents. Laurie Zimmerman of the *Times* of London (New York office), Jenny Phillips in Tokyo, and above all Ron Butler in Stuttgart have contributed enormously to the material on the United States, Japan, and Germany, respectively. Janet Langmaid and Lyn Amidan of the Wiener Library were most helpful in my quest for the elusive William Keppler.

Leonard Setright submitted the whole book to his quizzical and rigorous gaze from the technical standpoint; Karl Ludvigsen and George Ulrich were also kind enough to read some of the chapters.

No thanks at all are due to General Motors, which, for reasons of its own, refused to give me any access to anyone connected with the most technically interesting program undertaken by the company for many a long year.

Contents

"When a new idea is first propounded, in the beginning every man objects, and the poor inventor runs the gauntlet of all petulant wits, every man finding his several flaws, no man approving it—now not one out of a hundred outlives this torture, and those that do are at great length so changed by the various contrivances of others that not any one man can pretend to the invention of the whole, nor will agree about their respective shares in the parts."

—Sir William Petty
England, seventeenth century

"Is the invention the idea, or the first conception of using the idea, or the actual utilization of the idea?"

—*The Sources of Invention*
by John Jewkes, David Sawers, and Richard Stillerman
England, twentieth century

Wankel

Introduction

A fine summer day in 1964 found me at the beautiful English racetrack at Goodwood, in the shadow of the Sussex downs. It was an agreeable half day's work for a journalist to examine an absurd new idea, the so-called Wankel engine, from the little-known German auto company NSU. Buzzing around the racetrack in the small open sports car in which the engine had been installed, I suddenly saw the point of the thing. It started off quietly, and the more the car accelerated the more it sounded, not like a *proper* car engine, but like a sewing machine. Instead of *boing-boing*, it went *mmmmmmmmmm*.

The first drive in a rotary-engined car is always disconcerting, for we are all conditioned to the idea that engines get noisier as they go faster. A Wankel, of course, does not. At first you are surprised and worried; then you relax and marvel at the rotary revolution.

I awoke from my dream of the rotary-driven future to see a small worried group of German engineers peering into the engines of the two other rotary vehicles on the track, and realized there would be some difficulties to overcome before the engine was ready for sale.

The difficulties should have been obvious when, four years later, I next came across the engine when testing that glamorous and unhappy machine, the RO80, also made by NSU.

After trying out the car, I had lunch with a slight intense man in dark glasses who spoke the precise, formal English common to well-brought-up Europeans. He was continually interrupted by phone calls from Paris, London, and Munich. He was not an executive or a director of NSU, but was treated with great deference by all concerned. His name was Max Adolphus Bunford, and before lunch was over he was off.

Clearly this was no ordinary engine, and no ordinary set of people was involved in it. There was an element of mystery in everything about the Wankel. And the further I delved into the

11

Wankel story, the more mysterious, elusive, and convoluted it appeared.

The story would be far different—and infinitely less intriguing—if Felix Wankel's ideas had been unsound. They were not and are not. The rotary engine he devised—simple, quiet, free from vibration— has enormous potential. Indeed, had the rotary engine been developed seventy years before the piston engines we now use, and not seventy years after, anyone trying to sell the idea of the heavy, noisy, complex reciprocating engine, using fuel far more refined than that required by a rotary, would be laughed out of court.

Yet even now, some twenty years after Dr. Wankel first dreamed up the exact configuration of the rotary engine named after him, the motor industry is still not converted to its virtues. Only two man-ufacturers in the world actually make the engine, and a couple more are planning to. The men who have taken it up are not the ordinary type of organization men. Inevitably autocratic, they are often ac-cused of simply squandering their shareholders' money on an im-practical dream. The curious history of the Wankel is the story of the better mousetrap that had a hell of a job finding a market.

The history of the Wankel bridges several generations of capi-talism. It involves big, modern corporations, each with its own mystique and its own internal conflicts, but it also brings in in-dividual wheeler-dealers who seem to have strayed from the more casual days of nineteenth-century capitalism, before the era of or ganograms and management consultants.

Many of these characters, particularly those involved in the technical development of the engine, have proved jealous of each other's work, and these feelings in some cases have led to lawsuits. If many of the contributors to the Wankel saga have received neither fame nor financial reward, a few participants, including the inventor himself, have done very well for themselves.

Despite the Wankel's problems, and its picaresque progress through the capitalist world, the rotary engine remains an invention of great engineering sense and beauty, its elegance perceivable by the layman as well as by the qualified engineer. It remains, too, the most versatile idea for propelling earth-bound vehicles to have been developed since the reciprocating engine was first introduced, nearly ninety years ago, by Messrs. Daimler and Benz.

The story of the Wankel is, of course, not yet finished. There are other reasons, too, why this account cannot pretend to be a definitive history of the engine. Although I have tried to explain the technical developments of the engine since it was first sketched out on Dr. Felix Wankel's kitchen table, I have deliberately kept the technical explanations to a minimum, introducing them only when necessary to explain the engine's development and in a simplified form appropriate in a book written for a nontechnical audience.

But in the case of the Wankel, to simplify is to distort. There are a dozen technical aspects of the rotary on which a separate—and controversial—volume could be written, and almost every episode in the history of its development admits more than one interpretation. Appropriately, the story of the rotary contains no straight lines; everything about it is contradictory, confused, and contentious. And no aspect of the rotary's story is more complex than its inventor, Felix Wankel.

Felix Wankel

"It is nobody's business to pry into my personal and financial life and experiences."

—Felix Wankel, 1974

No one who has ever met Felix Wankel is indifferent to him. His admirers see him as one of the most original mechanical brains of the twentieth century, a self-taught genius with the practical imaginative eye to solve engineering problems—for Wankel is impatient of pure theory. "Imagination costs nothing," he has said. "We could also build square locomotives or fly to Mars." Wankel's own estimate of himself is that he is the successor to two great German engineers who have made two fundamental contributions to modern automotive engineering: Dr. Nikolaus Otto, who designed the Otto four-stroke cycle that made the internal-combustion engine a practical possibility, and Dr. Rudolf Diesel, who invented the compression-combustion engine named after him.

Hostile witnesses—who include many of those who have worked or negotiated with him—consider him, at the least, egocentric, ungrateful, and unappreciative of other people's work. The more extreme will, absurdly, deny him any credit for the engine bearing his name.

"He has never," says one opponent, "built an engine that runs or contributed to one. . . . Technically he has nothing to be proud of. . . . He has no great technical understanding."

The German engineering establishment always regarded him as an amateur and fanatic and has certainly never rushed to acclaim him although he is the author of the most important invention since the war.

More judicious but still hostile observers contend that Wankel has been apparently reluctant to develop his ideas beyond a certain point. Once any model has been proved workable, and the first examples are actually running, he abandons his mechanical children, ignores their further problems, and confines himself to sarcastic kibitzing of the lesser mortals who are trying to turn his ideas into commercial practice.

He has said disdainfully of the present book: "I know of no accounts of engineering inventions where the commercial side has been made to play the prominent part."

In personal terms his attitude leads him to exhibit profound jealousy and ingratitude toward those who have helped him. His neighbors at Lindau, the small city on Lake Constance where he has lived for forty years, call him "Der Schuldendoktor"—the debt doctor—saying that, for all his promises of help, he has not given away any of his fortune (now over $20 million) to anything useful. Instead, Wankel has founded a cats' and dogs' home. On the other hand, around $400,000 a year supports the research of the controversial Manfred von Ardenne, who runs an institute in East Germany that explores new methods for the treatment of cancer.

Amid the accusations of personal inadequacies, Wankel continues to keep his fertile, inventive brain in full employment. He lives modestly (until he was given a rotary-engined RO80, his only car was an ancient Borgward family saloon), and, at the age of seventy-three, he is still hard at work till late at night in his institute, a one-storied glass-fronted building built to his own design, facing Lake Constance, and packed with modern machinery and test beds for new inventions. This reality is far from his critics' picture of the eccentric and futile millionaire amateur.

Wankel has devoted much of the past fifteen years to another revolutionary idea: a boat which would be the marine equivalent of a fast passenger car. His rotary-engined cigar-shaped Zisch-boat ("zisch" is German for "zip") can streak evenly through, under, and over the waves, air- and watertight when submerged, able to cope with the roughest waters. He sees no reason why these boats should not cross the Atlantic, fueled from a series of floating gas stations. ("But just imagine," Wankel told a startled visitor, "if someone had suggested in the year 1900 to put up gas stations in the Odenwald forest.")

Although he has done little to make his most famous invention a practical proposition, he has looked beyond its immediate problems. He has designed a rotary diesel engine, solving difficulties that had baffled other engineers by scrapping the configuration he had devised for the rotary gasoline engine. Recently, he has emerged with an ingenious, imaginative, but, as always, technically impeccable solution to the problem of his offspring's allegedly excessive fuel consumption—a supercharger driven by the engine's exhaust gases.

Felix Wankel is no ordinary man. Yet his life story resembles that of many thousands of his contemporaries.

Wankel was born on August 13, 1902, in Lahr, a small city in Swabia, a district in southwestern Germany near the French border, where he has lived all his life. The Swabians are somewhat of a joke among Germans, who think them crude, provincial, heavy, and somewhat stupid. But even Germans from the Rhineland and Berlin admit that the modern internal combustion engine was perfected by the Swabians—Otto, Daimler, and Benz. And the company named after the last two, with headquarters in Stuttgart, Swabia's biggest city, produces one of the world's finest cars, the Mercedes-Benz.

Felix Wankel's father, Rudolf, was a civil servant, a commissioner in the forestry department—for Swabia includes much of the Schwarzwald, Germany's great Black Forest. Rudolf volunteered at the outbreak of World War I and was killed during the first month of fighting, leaving Felix fatherless at the age of twelve. Rudolf Wankel left a fair amount of money, but, as was the experience of many middle-class German families, it was wiped out by the horrific inflation of the early 1920s, when suitcases of marks were required for the simplest household purchases.

Felix Wankel did not go to a technical high school or follow an engineering apprenticeship, the usual path taken by mechanically-minded German children. In fact, he admits that "the entire school business bored me" and, although "good in German history and Latin, I was very untalented in mathematics." Even in his youth he had what he calls a "one-sided talent" for technical drawings and for making models from the drawings.

Instead of going on to a university, Wankel went to work in 1921 at a university booksellers' in Heidelberg specializing in scientific works. But he did not sell books. He started off in the company's print shop, until an early kidney rupture made it inadvisable for him to work with lead type. He ended up working in a storeroom, where he devised a new method of storing books (on a square pattern that enabled them to be stacked from floor to ceiling without tumbling down). There he was able to do his private work and technical drawing without disturbance. At the same time, he attended night school and took correspondence courses.

In 1924, when he was twenty-two, Felix Wankel caught the rotary bug. His motivation can only be guessed at, for he refuses to talk about his early life, claiming that curiosity will be satisfied when he publishes his autobiography. Whatever the reason, he became obsessed, as so many great engineers had been before him, with the idea of using rotary movement to produce power more efficiently than is possible with the reciprocating-piston engine. It was, on the face of it, an absurdly arrogant notion that a self-taught engineer working as an apprentice bookseller in a small town in southwest Germany could solve problems that had baffled three centuries of efforts by some of the world's best scientific brains.

2

The Rotary Dream

"The histories of nearly all the machines used by engineers at
the present day are happy. They tell of a steady development
from rudimentary beginnings and record a series of successful
adventures as greater and greater things were attempted. . . . But
the story of positive acting rotary machines is an exception. For
over one hundred years engineers and others struggled to bring
into successful use a principle with undoubted advantages but
with hidden defects of a serious character."

—*The Engineer* magazine, January 1939

Could a self-taught engineer design a rotary engine? For 350
years—since the dawn of modern scientific time—large numbers of
engineers, including some of the most eminent names of the nineteenth century, have struggled to produce one. By 1924, when
Wankel started work, it seemed fair to assert that the advantages of a
purely rotary engine, like so many other theoretically desirable
improvements, could not be realized in engineering practice.

The advantages of a rotary engine were obvious. A wheel,
whether on a car, a train, or a bicycle, goes around; it does not go up
and down (reciprocating motion); it does not oscillate (swing
regularly from side to side like a pendulum). What could be more
natural than a rotary engine? For any other means of propulsion,
whether reciprocating or oscillating, involves translating the
pumping or pendulumlike motion to a rotary form. This inevitably
complicates the mechanism and leads to a loss of valuable energy,
used up by the translating apparatus involved.

No wonder, therefore, that inventors and engineers thought

about rotary pumps and engines for centuries before the nineteenth century, when the theoretically less efficient reciprocating principle was made a practical proposition—first in a steam locomotive, then, in the last years of the century, as an internal-combustion engine. Some of the technology necessary to make rotary engines possible was invented long before the steam engine and had been used in pumps. This made the failure to construct a practical rotary engine even more frustrating to designers. For, in theory, a pump can be converted into an engine simply by putting the power inside the unit, rather than applying it from outside. But until Wankel appeared on the scene, the translation had never been made in an engine that could be considered seriously—but not for want of trying.

Wankel's own book on the subject catalogs hundreds of rotary shapes that had been tried out over the centuries. The British Patent Office contains over 2,000 patents covering the design of rotary engines and pumps taken out before 1910. The anonymous writer in *The Engineer* pointed to the "endless variety" of combinations possible with a rotary engine, for the word "rotary" covers many different types of movement; indeed, the author listed eleven different types, each of which had numerous subdivisions. The rotor supplying the power could be of a hundred different shapes, as could the stationary housing, or container, for the engine. The very diversity of opportunity provided one good reason both for the boundless optimism of successive generations of inventors and for their failure.

As *The Engineer*'s writer pointed out:

It is probable that it is this very variety that has been the curse of the positive acting rotary. For an inventor, finding by experiment that his first scheme was faulty, was less likely to persist with it and by steady minor alteration to improve it than to turn his attention to another variety, and experience further disappointment. By contrast the attention of succeeding generations of engineers has been continuously concentrated for a century and a half on the pistons, connecting rod and crank mechanism so that as a result of persistent minor improvement it can today be so constructed as to run at speeds which the first users would have regarded as fantastic.

The honor of being the first on the rotary field is generally awarded to a Genoese soldier, who in 1588 published a book entitled *Le diverse e artificiose macchine del Capitane Agostino Ramelli.*

Among the gallant captain's hundred or so "diverse and ingenious contrivances," two, at least, are recognizable as rotary engines. The power was provided by a sort of paddle arrangement attached to a drum, which itself revolved eccentrically inside a casing.

But the first practical rotary movement was completely different. The seventeenth-century engineer Pappenheim devised a pump that involved two paddle-shaped parts. These intermeshed but moved in opposite directions, thus pushing water through the casing in which they were housed. Pappenheim's idea was used to provide the power for the fountains of Rome, Prague, and Salzburg. His mechanism was again taken up at the end of the eighteenth century, when engineers in general first became infected with rotary fever.

At that time rotary power was needed, as never before, for stationary (and later mobile) steam engines. Engineers led by James Watt, the inventor of the steam engine, tried out rotary designs first and were suspicious of reciprocating designs. Watt designed a number of rotary engines, none of which worked. He did encounter one difficulty with a modern ring to it. His workmen often would go out and get patents in their own names. One of them, William Murdoch, tried unsuccessfully to adapt Pappenheim's design to produce power.

Following Watt's example, many eighteenth- and nineteenth-century engineers had a crack at designing a rotary engine: Joseph Bramah, inventor of the modern flush toilet, the unpickable lock that bears his name, the screw propeller, and the hydraulic press; Routledge, who thought up the slide rule; and Sir Charles Parsons, the pioneer of the steam turbine, were among the roll call of famous names who failed to produce a workable rotary. It was left to a less known man, Elijah Galloway, to produce a design in which an oval-shaped rotor rotated within a circular chamber, a formula far nearer to Felix Wankel's eventual solution than any other designed in the 118 years between the two ideas.

But all the designs failed to solve the problem of sealing. Designers realized that in a reciprocating engine, the only gap to be sealed is the simple ring between the piston and the walls of the cylinder in which it moves up and down. In a rotary engine, the whole circumference requires sealing. If the packing is too loose, power is lost through leakage; if too tight, it is lost through friction. The worse the leak, the lower the power. Hemp, cotton, yarn, or plaits of yarn were tried, but use of these, it was found, ' produces great friction and loss of power." No wonder "the problems of packing and uneven wear were avoided," according to one expert, "rather than overcome, and those machines that survived were those that least needed tightness of packing and precision of manufacture."

Despite these limitations, some rotary machines worked, but mostly as pumps, blowers, compressors, meters, and compressed-air motors.

The late nineteenth century saw the first attempt to classify the types of rotary power and their potential. Franz Reuleaux, the great dynamist, tried, as Felix Wankel noted in his book on rotary engines:

... to bring order into the chaos of the rotary piston machine field which he described in great detail in his books and writings. His proposed classification was, however, a little too artificial for the purpose of imparting to the designer the characteristics of a multitude of differing machines.

In the end even Reuleaux became so confused that he wrote a book devoted largely to proving that a rotary steam engine could never work, but Wankel acknowledges that his major work contained "so many examples and illustrations that it remained for decades the best-known scientific review and collection of this type of machine."

By then, Dr. Nikolaus Otto and his successors had established the dominance of the four-cycle motor. In successive stages, gas and air are let into a cylinder (induction), then compressed (the compression stage), then burned (combustion), and finally let out again (exhaust). The development of engines for cars, and then for airplanes, based on the Otto cycle, ironically gave a lease on life to what might be called "bastard" rotary engines. In these the power was provided by the movement of pistons in the cylinder back and forth in a straight line, but the cylinders, indeed the whole engine, rotated. The best-known example was the Gnome le Rhone aeroengine, much used in fighter planes in World War I. In this and other "rotary" engines, the cylinders and the propeller rotated around a stationary shaft. This idea provided a lighter, more balanced, and much more compact power unit. But it did not produce rotary combustion with all its advantages. The same arrangement was used in the first rotary car ever made in the United States, the Adams-Farwell, built in Dubuque, Iowa, in 1904. Although its engine had three cylinders rotating around a fixed shaft, again the power was not provided by rotary movement.

The dominance of the four-stroke engine posed yet another complication for rotary enthusiasts: Now they had to add to their requirements the need for their design to provide a four-stroke cycle automatically. Sometimes they had to cheat and use valves, as on an orthodox engine. These provided four-stroke motion, but even the best involved precisely those mechanical complications that a true rotary engine is supposed to avoid. At the turn of the century, for instance, an American, John Cooley, devised a number of rotary configurations. None provided a natural four-cycle movement, but one design with a four-sided rotor in a five-sided chamber proved interesting enough to be taken up fifty years later by both the French Renault company and American Motors.

The list of names of hopeful rotary designers since Cooley is long: De Lavaud . . . Sauveur and Fiebig . . . Moineau . . . Franzen and Fahlbeck. There was a scissor-action engine designed by a Swiss, Traugott Tschudi, and a German, Eugen Kauertz. And there was one design called the Virmel, after the first letters of the names of its inventors, Virginia and Melvin Rolfsmeyer, a couple from Nebraska. None worked.°

But, despite all these failures, there was no inherent reason why a rotary engine should not be made. The theoretical problem—devising a formula that naturally provided a four-stroke movement—and the biggest practical drawback—the absence of suitable sealing systems—were difficult. But, to quote *The Engineer* again:

Much more complicated mechanisms have been made reliable as the result of the unremitting efforts of generations of engineers striving toward a single end . . . and we see no reason why similar efforts directed toward perfecting the rotary should not yield equally encouraging results.

° Neither have the many ideas put forward since the Wankel itself became a practical proposition. These include the Anglo-American Karol-Ansdale-Anidyne, the Sarich from western Australia, the Rotodane from Sydney, Fred Erickson's migratory combustion-chamber engine, Jack L. Gilbert's "loose-leaf" reed engine, Ronald Ryea's swing-piston Ryenco, and a motor devised by a gentleman with the unpromising name of V. G. Null.

Before the help of hordes of engineers could be enlisted, one man had to solve the two outstanding problems involved. By the laws of probability, the most likely candidate to do so would be the first man to succeed in analyzing the chaos that surrounded the rotary engine and devising a system that would logically categorize the whole rotary field—the task Reuleaux, one of the greatest dynamists of his time, had so notably failed to achieve.

3

Keppler

"Keppler deserves to be better known to the world than he is
for his part in laying the basic economic foundation for Hitler's
invasions and wars of aggression. Keppler learned from World
War I that Germany needed to be self-sufficient in certain critical
raw materials to be successful in another war."
      —Prosecution lawyer, Nuremberg war crime trial, 1949

Although Wankel had already set up his own workshop, for two
years after he started his lifework on the problem of rotary motion he
continued to be employed by the Heidelberg booksellers. In 1926 he
left the booksellers—whether he was sacked or went voluntarily is
unclear—and has subsequently never worked for anyone else.

From the beginning he combined practical and experimental
work—mainly on rotary valves and the problems involved in sealing
reciprocating engines—which earned enough to enable him to work
on a systematic study of rotary motion. Wankel's first sketches for a
rotary engine date from 1927, before he had begun any serious work
on the sealing problems involved. Subsequently he only strayed once
from the straight and narrow path of true rotary motion: In the first
patent he was granted, in 1929, he copied previous generations and
dodged the sealing problem by contriving an engine that would use
the sort of simple, circular piston rings fitted on orthodox reciprocating engines.

For the next twenty years, Wankel made his living, and a distinguished name for himself, by concentrating on the problem of sealing
reciprocating engines, first on motorcycles, then on engines for a
variety of uses, including cars, aircraft, and, at the end of World War

25

II, torpedoes. Between 1929 and 1931, having bought four cheap secondhand machine tools, he developed more than a dozen devices to test the principle of making rotary valves. He produced a motorcycle that ran with a disk-valved engine and an engine operated by a cylindrical rotary valve.

In order to survive, politically and industrially, and to retain his cherished independence, Wankel needed a patron. In an astonishing stroke of luck, he found a man in his home town who possessed exactly the right qualities to be the perfect father figure for a struggling, strongly nationalist, and visionary inventor.

William Keppler was a well-to-do Swabian businessman. After spending nine months in a sanitarium in his twenties because of heart trouble, he had gone to manage a gelatine factory near Heidelberg for a distant relative, just before World War I. He became a fervent nationalist—especially on the issue of German self-sufficiency in raw materials. He also developed paternalistic antiunion views on industrial relations that chimed perfectly with Hitler's. He had met Hitler in 1927 and became one of the first businessmen to join what was then a very populist party overtly hostile to big business. He remained an unabashed Nazi throughout his life, defending Hitler as an exceptionally kind man, even as he stood in the dock at Nuremberg.

By the early thirties, Keppler had become one of the most influential men around Hitler. He was one of the first to urge him to reverse his economic policies and woo big business. Hitler commissioned him to sound out potential sympathizers within industry and form them into what became known as "Keppler's Circle of Friends." Keppler was also deeply involved in the intrigues during the winter of 1932–33 involving Von Papen and Schleicher. In 1934, when Hitler acquired supreme power, Keppler was rewarded with an office next to Hitler's, the sonorous title of "economic adviser of the Fuhrer in the Reich chancellery," and his own small department, the "Büro Keppler." But within a year Keppler's direct economic influence had waned—for Hitler's major use for him had clearly been as a middleman in reconciling the formerly hostile forces of big business to the Nazi party. By 1936 he had been totally overshadowed in the economic sphere by Dr. Schacht, but, throughout the period of Nazi rule, Keppler continued to be used as a high-level contact man and troubleshooter by Hitler.

As Hitler's personal emissary, he was put in charge of many of

Germany's subversive efforts, first in Austria and then in Czecho-slovakia. Keppler was deeply involved in setting up the famous Hermann Goering Werke, designed to exploit some of Germany's uneconomically low-grade iron-ore deposits. As a state secretary and honorary general in the SS, he organized the resettlement of German families in occupied Europe during the war. (His face peered out of newspapers published in occupied Poland, incongruously unmilitary under his SS cap.)

In 1928, Keppler met Wankel and saw in him a "technically original and patriotic young man worthy of support." Like so many other middle-class Germans whose family fortunes had been wiped out in the inflation of the 1920s, Wankel had become a supporter of national socialism, joined the Hitler Youth (where he met his wife), and then the Nazi party.

It was Keppler's support which ensured that Wankel received official recognition for his often way-out ideas. Wankel has claimed that he left the party in 1932 and that he subsequently stumbled across—and publicized—some corrupt dealings by the local Gauleiter. As a result, he was imprisoned. He was released a few months later, Wankel claims, through the efforts of Keppler and Dr. Otto Nibel, then the chief engineer of Daimler-Benz. It was the first of many services Keppler was to render Wankel over the next twenty-five years. Wankel's first contract on his release from prison in 1933 was with Daimler-Benz. But after a year he quarreled with the then general manager, and he moved on to work with BMW (Bayerischen Motoren Werke) in Munich, for whom he developed a piston engine with rotating valves. These were superior to the usual reciprocating design because they allowed the engine to be far more compact. In 1936 his work was considered important enough for him to be invited by Goering's Aviation Ministry to join the Central Research Establishment in Berlin. But Wankel, as ever, preferred to retain his independence, and he already had a reputation as an awkward colleague. So Keppler arranged for the government to set him up in his own workshop, in a town called Lindau, where he has lived ever since. Already, in the ten years after he had set up on his own, Wankel had worked out and patented his revolutionary ideas for sealing engines to ensure that gases did not leak. It was the sealing methods he devised in the late 1920s and the early 1930s, in fact, that form his most original contribution to automotive science. (They also formed the key to his subsequent fortune, since in the patents he took out in the 1930s he covered all the possible applications of his ideas for sealing engines and compressors of all sorts, whether they were reciprocating or truly rotary devices.)

Wankel realized that to seal an engine satisfactorily required some other method than sliding two surfaces together, however well they were machined and finished. There would always be much friction and, consequently, rapid wear that would lead to significant leakage. Seals, therefore, should be a separate element in the design of an engine, what he called a "packing body." But it was also crucial not to make this "body" too big, or too wide, or there would be considerable loss of power again because of the friction generated. So the seals had to be as small as possible. Wankel devised thin, metallic strips or plates, tough enough to do the job, but not too thick or heavy to create problems of excess friction.

Wankel also made use of the pressure of the gas trying to escape from the chamber to be sealed. Previously this had been regarded as a hostile force. But Wankel used the gas itself to apply the necessary pressure on the seals, rather than the very strong springs needed previously. To this day, all the rotary engines made according to Wankel's principles use springs merely as supports and as a way of keeping the sealing elements in position, not as the principal means of preventing leakage. The pressure of the gas being contained within the chamber by the sealing elements actually provides the force necessary to keep itself in.

Wankel went further than outlining the theory: He produced, for the first time in engineering history, a method of sealing a rectangular space. Previously, seals had been circular—as they still are in reciprocating engines, where they are, after all, one or more simple rings fitting tightly around the piston, like a wedding ring around a finger. Wankel succeeded in sealing a rectangle against gas leakage by means of "trunnions" at the corners—pegs with holes cut in them into which the thin, small seals he had devised slipped securely.

The first true rotary engine Wankel ever designed was also patented during the 1930s. It was a complicated, cumbersome affair, with two housings and rotors, one to compress the air, the other for combustion purposes. The two rotors were curiously shaped, and both were needed to provide a four-stroke cycle, but the engine proved that a sealing grid using Wankel's thin strips—some straight, some curved, secured at the corners with his cylindrical plungers— would retain the gas in a container.

The Luftwaffe was not interested in the rotary engine, but Wankel's ideas on rotary disk valves ° were of great interest in the development of more compact and powerful aircraft engines, and most of Wankel's time immediately before and during the war was spent on this problem—in collaboration with Daimler-Benz. Wankel was particularly concerned with trying to replace the standard valve, made of an alloy containing nickel—a metal in desperately short supply in wartime Germany. He saw that previous designs of rotary valves had failed because they had to be made too precisely. Instead, he proposed to use flexible rings pressing down on the surface to be sealed, and these did not have to be made to such exact specifications.

Wankel's war work was not directly related to his life's dream of making a truly rotary engine, which, by definition, would not have any valves of any description and would rely purely on the movement of its rotary parts to allow the fuel and air in and the exhaust gases out of the combustion chamber. But at least he was allowed to continue his work on sealing systems. (During this period he was nicknamed "Deutschlands Abdichter"—Germany's sealer.)

He also established a wide range of contacts within German industry. By the end of the war, he was working with Junkers, the aircraft company, on a torpedo engine that would propel a torpedo at forty miles per hour. Its theoretical compactness required an entirely new kind of valve system.

He also had contracts with Borsig—a compressor manufacturer as well as Germany's largest maker of railway rolling stock—and, in 1944, designed an adjustable rotary compressor. He also worked closely with Goetze, which was (and still is) Germany's leading maker of piston rings. During the war Goetze produced IKA, a very tough iron alloy, which later proved useful for developers of Wankel's rotary engines. Wankel's personal wartime contacts would be equally useful to him in the 1950s when he was trying to interest firms in the idea of a rotary engine.

But in 1945, Wankel's dream engine still seemed just that. Lindau was occupied by the French. His institute had been dismantled, his drawings destroyed, and he himself was arrested. But, in fact, the abrupt changes in his life and circumstances set him off on the road

---

° These are flat disks, with holes, that revolve, providing air and gas to a cylinder at the appropriate moment in the firing cycle.

that, within a decade, led to the production of his revolutionary
rotary engine.

For in adversity he was forced back to first principles. Wankel
had started work on his catalog in 1938, but had to start again from
scratch after the war, at first in the privacy of his home, then, after
1951, in his rebuilt institute. But in the end he succeeded, where
Reuleaux had failed, in devising a system of classifying the thousands
of possible configurations for a rotary engine.

The result of his work was not published until 1963. It indicates
clearly how the search for a rotary engine had been conducted.
Wankel had had the brilliant idea of classifying engines according to
the type of movement of their working parts. There were reciprocating engines, which included motors with an oscillating, pen-
dulum-type movement as well as the up-and-down motion characteristic of reciprocating internal-combustion engines; and engines
where all the movement was circular and all the parts remained at
the same angle to the engine's center of gravity—which they can
effectively do with purely circular motion. These, classed as single-
rotation machines, were always his favorite, for they provided the
simplest and most efficient type of movement. If all movement was
in one direction and on one path, and all the forces involved were
completely balanced, then none of the energy was wasted. In engineering terms, this provided the most "elegant" solution to the
problem of rotary movement, since to engineers elegance is equated
with simplicity. By this criterion, the "planetary-rotation machines," which formed another category, were "bastard" rotary
machines because an element of swing was superimposed on the
rotary movement. There was a fourth category of "rotating-piston"
machines, which could be divided into either single- or planetary-
rotation machines. But all this work was purely theoretical. To
translate it into practice, Wankel required a backer, preferably one
from the auto industry—an unlikely enough prospect in the strait-
ened conditions of postwar Germany.

Nevertheless, Wankel's luck held.

4

Von Heydekampf

> "There are three ways of ruining myself: women, gambling, and inventors. The last is the least agreeable but most certain."
> —BARON DE ROTHSCHILD

In early 1951 there was a general amnesty for all but the most notorious Nazi criminals as a result of the outbreak of the Korean War and the consequent desire of the American government to enlist the help of the German people in the fight against what was seen as a worldwide Communist threat. Despite his prominence, even Keppler was included, and in April he was released from prison. But he had never been a well man and in July entered the Robert Bosch Hospital in Stuttgart. In the next bed was an executive from NSU, a small motorcycle company. In the course of conversation, Keppler mentioned that he knew an inventor who had devised a rotating disk valve that might be useful to NSU in their efforts to construct more compact engines. From this casual remark came the contract between NSU and Wankel that was to give the Wankel engine to the world.

At first glance, there were many other companies more likely than NSU to take on Wankel and his ideas. The company had grown up in the small town of Neckarsulm, forty miles northwest of Stuttgart. NSU—short for Neckarsulm Strickmachinen Union—had been building Italian Fiat cars under license since 1904, but in the 1920s it had become connected with a Jewish financier called Shapiro. When his empire crashed at the end of the decade, the pieces were picked up by the Dresdner Bank, one of the three banks that dominated the German financial scene. In the 1930s, Fiat, the Italian auto maker,

31

took over the NSU plant in Heilbronn, near Neckarsulm, to assemble their cars in Germany. In an incautious letter, the NSU chief executive of the time gave Fiat "permission to make cars under the name NSU/Fiat," a loosely worded phrase that was to cause NSU much anguish and some money when they started to build cars again at the end of the 1950s.

Unusually, the company's main factory was still standing at the end of the war. It got off to an early start, first of all repairing war equipment for the American occupying forces, then repairing bicycles. In the late 1940s, it began to manufacture small motorcycles. When Keppler told NSU of Wankel's work, NSU had just started producing the two types of motorcycles that would make the company famous. One was the Quickly moped, a tiny fifty-cubic-centimeter motorized bicycle that was the ideal form of transport for a Germany struggling to get to work by the cheapest possible means of personal transport. NSU made Quicklys by the million, but it became even better known for its racing motorcycles, with which it won two successive world championships in the early 1950s. (It then turned to breaking speed records in an effort to keep its name in the headlines.)

Three key men were responsible for NSU's success. They were also jointly responsible for the steadfast backing of Wankel that ensured the development of his ideas. They were Dr. Victor Frankenberger, who was in charge of the production and technical side of the company, Dr. Walter Froede, the chief engineer, who was the designer of the championship motorcycles, and Gerd Stieler von Heydekampf, NSU's chief executive.

Von Heydekampf is an engineer, the son of a Prussian regular army officer who had worked in the United States during the depression. On his return he became manager of Adam Opel, the German subsidiary of General Motors, and then the biggest auto manufacturer in Germany. During the war he had an even bigger job running the gigantic Henschel Organization, which made tanks and locomotives and employed 60,000 workers. He was one of the dozen top production executives whom Albert Speer consulted in strict secrecy in 1945 to try to sabotage Hitler's scorched-earth policy that called for the destruction of German industry.

After the war von Heydekampf was interrogated and imprisoned for a few months. Because of his importance to the German war effort, Heydekampf's denazification had taken longer than that of more junior executives; for example, he had been unable to take up the job of running the heap of rubble that was the Volkswagen plant at Wolfsburg when it was offered to him, but had recommended his successor at Opel, Hans Nordhoff, instead. In 1949, he got his first job as a traveling salesman for NSU under the then chief executive, Herr Niegtsch, who had formerly worked under Heydekampf at Henschel. After Niegtsch's death in 1951, Heydekampf was the obvious successor. Because of the chance encounter with Keppler in the Stuttgart hospital, he knew about Wankel's work, and in the beginning of August 1951 Frankenberger invited Wankel to come to Neckarsulm to talk about a possible research contract. Typically, Wankel insisted that NSU send someone to Lindau instead. Finally, at the beginning of October, Froede, the chief engineer, visited Wankel and talked over his ideas. All Wankel had to show were drawings, pictures, and reports, but Froede was sufficiently impressed to recommend to Heydekampf and Frankenberger that they should take up some of Wankel's ideas for future use in motorcycle engines. He also thought that NSU should make some form of contract with Wankel—who was then being financed in a small way by both Daimler-Benz and Goetze, the manufacturer of piston rings and engine seals. Froede did not mention to his superiors that Wankel had also talked about research on rotary engines and hydrofoils. He probably thought it would give the impression that Wankel was a little too much of an eccentric for comfort. After reading Froede's report, Frankenberger himself went to Lindau, where he spent eight hours talking to Wankel, who again started talking about rotary engines as well as the rotary valves and disks that NSU were originally interested in.

In December, Wankel finally came to Neckarsulm and signed a contract to develop a motorcycle engine with valves that slid round to open and shut (a "rotary slide" engine). He would be paid $500 a month—a sum later increased to $750. In two years, with the assistance of an NSU engineer, Wankel designed the engine.

From the start, NSU had disagreements with Wankel, who wrongly thought, for example, that the rotary disk valve engine did not need a proper cooling system. But von Heydekampf still recalls "what fun Wankel was to talk to in those days," and on the whole the company and the inventor remained pleased with each other.

Wankel's rotary valve reciprocating engine worked well enough.

But in March 1953 Wankel had been told firmly that NSU was not prepared to back him in the development of a rotary engine. Even those NSU engineers who supported his ideas about rotary sliding valve engines thought that the rotary engine was an eccentric whim and technically unfeasible. Even if such an engine could be made to work, they all agreed it would take up to ten years to develop it, and NSU simply did not have the available funds.

NSU's discouraging attitude provoked Wankel to look elsewhere. Shortly after he went to work for NSU, he had approached Dr. Ferry Porsche, the head of the Porsche sports car firm, with detailed drawings of a possible rotary engine. Porsche's reaction was typical: He noted how much development work needed to be done, and Porsche, one of the smallest German auto manufacturers, simply did not have the necessary resources to devote to such a task.

Wankel's wartime connections with Goetze and Borsig were still in force during this period. By the terms of the contracts, any of his work on automotive or other sealing devices could be exploited by either company. At the end of 1953, Wankel told NSU that Borsig was interested in a rotary-piston compressor and had offered Wankel a development contract. He pointed out that the machine he had in mind would have a very high compression and thus would be very suitable for development as an engine. But, at that point, von Heydekampf and his colleagues were still trying to concentrate Wankel's efforts on solving their problems and continued to discourage his more visionary ideas.

In January 1954, Wankel produced his bombshell—an idea which was both revolutionary and technically sound. At one of his routine meetings with NSU, he produced drawings which showed a rotor with three convex sides rotating in a double-circle housing—a bulbous triangle circling in a chamber shaped like a peanut (or like a pair of dumbbells with no real handle between them). These drawings contained, in essence, the geometry of the Wankel rotary engine as we know it today. Wankel's original idea was that both the rotor and the housing containing it would revolve. This would produce the perfectly circular motion with all the moving parts going in the same direction, of which he was so fond—a fondness based on the scientifically sound idea that only with purely circular motion do you eliminate all mechanical and dynamic inefficiency.

Precisely when this idea occurred to Wankel is uncertain. He says it happened immediately after Christmas 1953, while he was in a liverish state induced by too much Christmas pudding. In another version he claims he had had the idea in the back of his head since the 1920s. In any case, the design was christened the DKM 53, and Wankel set to work developing it. (DKM stands for Drehkolbenmotor, the German word for "rotary piston engine," and 53 referred to the year Wankel began to work on it.)

Froede advised Wankel to first build a compressor rather than an engine, but early in February, at a second meeting, Wankel pointed out that he had a contract with Borsig to develop a rotary engine as well as a compressor. Taking the hint, Frankenberger committed NSU to sharing in the development costs, and a comprehensive agreement was drawn up.

"A technical invention is nothing economically without a patent," said von Heydekampf, and NSU and Wankel agreed to investigate the patent situation.

Wankel was prepared to extend his contract with NSU—which at the time was only for rotary slide engines—to include true rotary engines. He did not ask for any additional money, instead insisting that the development work be done at Lindau—mainly to avoid the conflicts he foresaw if he tried to work with engineers from NSU who were used to orthodox engines. Finally, he asked NSU to induce his former chief designer, Ernest Hoeppner, to come and work at Lindau ("because I can't work without him"). Hoeppner, called "the Captain" because he came from the North German seaport of Bremen, was invaluable to Wankel. He was not an inventor, but a brilliant designer able to translate Wankel's ideas into practice. He had worked with Wankel during the war, and did so again until Hoeppner's death in 1967. Their relationship, however, was stormy. Wankel had always been jealous of other people's work, and the strain of working with Hoeppner, whose help he never fully acknowledged he needed, provoked numerous arguments.

Hoeppner started working with Wankel in March 1954, and within a few weeks, working largely on a makeshift drawing board in Wankel's kitchen, they had proved the vital points: The epitrochoid° shape of the housing in conjunction with the convex

---

° As a circle rolls along a straight line, a point along a radius of the circle traces a curve called a trochoid. If the generating circle rolls along another circle, the curve is called an epitrochoid. The extent to which the generating point is off center is called the eccentricity of the curve.

equilateral triangle of the rotor added up to a workable rotary engine.

The basic shape is actually sketched out in drawings dated April 18, 1956. In the words of Dieter Korp, the greatest expert on the history of the Wankel, "a working rotary engine had been discovered even though its components revolved only in the form of paper disks on an ingeniously conceived testing device." It was simplicity itself. The triangular rotor with convex sides rotated in the peanut-shaped housing, which itself rotated at two-thirds the speed of the rotor.

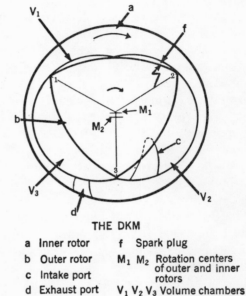

THE DKM

a	Inner rotor	f	Spark plug
b	Outer rotor	M_1 M_2	Rotation centers of outer and inner rotors
c	Intake port		
d	Exhaust port	V_1 V_2 V_3	Volume chambers

Because of the difference between the speeds, the gap between the rotor and the housing formed chambers of different sizes as the engine revolved, thus providing the compression needed to produce the combustion. As each face turned in the housing, it performed the four stages of the Otto cycle. Provided the gas intake, spark plug, and exhaust valve were correctly placed, each face would take in a gas-and-air mixture and compress it against the housing. The mixture would then be ignited when a spark was applied, and the resulting explosion would push the rotor around. In the fourth stage, the exhaust gas and air would be pushed out of the chamber. According to Jan Norbye, the author of a standard study of the engine:

Looking on the tip of the rotor as the hands of a clock, fresh mixture enters at 10 o'clock, compressing begins before 12 o'clock and reaches maximum at 3 o'clock. From 3 o'clock to 7:30 is pure combustion until the rotor uncovers the exhaust hole (port) and the exhaust phase begins.

For every single revolution of the rotor, there would be three power strokes—three revolutions of the drive shaft in the case of a car engine, for instance. Because all three faces of the rotor are working all the time, the single rotary engine packs the output of three cylinders of a reciprocating engine into one unit.

How to keep the gas and air in their separate chambers was to be one of the major stumbling blocks for the rotary engine. Wankel's original sealing system was devised during the 1930s. There were seals at the tips of each point of the triangular rotor (apex seals), and

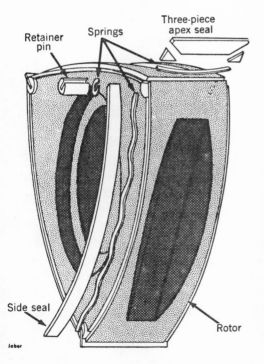

Retainer pin

Springs

Three-piece apex seal

Side seal

Rotor

laber

THE THREE-PIECE APEX SEAL

Two small triangular-shaped elements float freely against the main blade and provide effective seals at the corner of the chamber. Seals are pressed against the surface of the chamber by springs in combination with gas pressure that is bled into the region behind the seals. Retainer pins, key elements in the sealing system, have proved to be effective interfaces between the side seals and the apex seals.

there was a triangular grid around the sides of the triangular rotor (the "side seals"). The grid—originally a plate—was joined to the apex seals at the corners by Wankel's cylindrical plungers, the retaining pins that some authorities consider his most basic invention.

The real novelty was the shape; Wankel had devised dozens of different combinations in the postwar years. It was Professor Othmar Baier of the University of Stuttgart who discovered that the housing was an epitrochoid. The triangular rotor is a trochoid.

Although their organization seems simple, the DKMs—both the theoretical DKM 53 and then the DKM 54 designed by Wankel and Hoeppner and built by NSU—were extremely difficult to make practicable. To achieve his dream of purely rotary motion, Wankel had to allow both the rotor and the housing to revolve. Then the gas-and-air mixture passed through a hollow central shaft and from there through the rotor into the ever-changing spaces between the rotor and the outer housing. After the mixture had been naturally compressed as the chamber changed shape, it was ignited by one of the three spark plugs placed in the middle of each of the three faces of the rotor. The explosion produced a force that was transmitted through the outer housing, which was moving at two-thirds the speed of the rotor.

The method worked splendidly as a compressor because of its mechanical efficiency. Indeed, in the summer of 1954, NSU took one of its ridiculously small fifty-cubic-centimeter Quickly engines, souped it up by using a Wankel compressor housed in a mysterious black box, the contents of which were never revealed to the public, and set a speed record of nearly 120 miles per hour on the Bonneville Salt Flats in Utah, a record that still stands. These compressors were more than experimental units; for the first time Wankel's complete interlocking grid of seals—the result of his thirty years of work on sealing systems—was united with the triangular rotor and peanut-shaped chamber he had revealed earlier that year.

The DKM satisfied Wankel's insistence on the purest, simplest, and most "elegant" solution to the problem of rotary motion, but even Wankel and Hoeppner had an infernal job trying to turn the compressor into an engine by getting the fuel and air into the engine and the exhaust gas out. In addition, because both the rotor and its housing revolved, another stationary housing had to be provided in any engine fitted into a vehicle, a requirement which severely reduced one of the rotary's most obvious advantages—its theoretical lightness. And it was a nightmare actually igniting the compressed air and gas. The electrical impulses required to fire the spark plugs had to be transmitted through the outer rotor by an elaborate system of small metal strips. If spark plugs needed cleaning or replacement, merely getting at them was a major operation. Because they were housed actually on the rotor, the whole engine had to be dismantled.

Nonetheless, Wankel and Hoeppner persisted and, three years after they had realized that the DKM principle would work, produced a rotary engine. The biggest single problem they faced was the manufacturing of the housing that contained the rotor. The inside of this double circle had to be finished very accurately, to ensure that the rotor could revolve but that not too much gas was lost by seepage around the seals. Eventually, Hoeppner devised a special finishing machine to ensure that the cutting edge was always perpendicular to the curved surface it was grinding, the only way to ensure a smooth and accurate finish.

Froede and his chief engineer, Dr. Paschke, did not take any of Wankel's ideas for granted. They examined a number of alternative shapes, including a peanut-shaped rotor inside an almost circular inner rotor, a six-lobed rotor, and, more seriously, a four-lobed rotor inside a chamber with three compartments. This would have provided a six-cycle movement and thus more time for the power to be produced on each cycle; for the great advantage of the triangular rotor was that for a given size of combustion chamber, you required a shorter length of seals—a major asset in overcoming the crucial problem of leakage.

Without telling Wankel, Froede, Dr. Paschke, and the other NSU engineers took up another idea which Wankel had had at the same time as the DKM, but which he had discarded because it did not correspond to his rotary ideal. Froede, following this discarded idea of Wankel, proposed to simplify the construction of the engine by keeping the outer housing stationary and having only the rotor revolving. But in this case the movement of all the moving parts would not be purely rotary, for the rotor would waltz round inside the casing in a planetary movement, like the planets around the sun, or the irregular circle formed by a hula hoop going around a waist. The lurching movement created the variations in the size of the chambers needed to produce combustion. This "planetary" mechanism had been considered by Wankel as unsuitable for the very high speed of revolution attainable with a purely rotary machine. This was no mere theoretical disadvantage; the higher the revolutions per minute (rpm) of a motor, the greater the power that can be obtained from a given size of unit. Froede's development was christened the Kreiskolbenmotor—KKM for short and standing for "circuitous piston engine."

There was another disadvantage of the "planetary" machine. One of Wankel's major concerns was the reduction of the strains placed on the seals. Even the shape of the rotor had been fixed because it reduced the problem of sealing to the minimum. Because the DKM's movement was purely rotary and the two surfaces connected by the seals were both rotating in the same direction (albeit at different speeds), the crucial apex seals at the tips of the rotor were always at the same angle to the rotor, and centrifugal force pressed the seals of the rotor against the wall of the housing. With the KKM, on the other hand, the strain on the seals varied as the rotor waltzed around inside the chamber. And Wankel's fears for its effectiveness under these circumstances proved to be well founded.

But Froede's idea—what he called the "kinematic inversion" of Wankel's preferred design—simplified the construction of the engine enormously (see diagram). The outer housing was stationary, therefore a spark plug could be screwed into it—not into the rotor. The plug was then far more accessible. And to improve combustion, its angle or position on the housing could be altered—or another plug installed. In the same way, the inlet and outlet holes (ports) supplying the chambers created by the movement of the rotor as it lurched around could be placed almost anywhere. They could go on the flat side plates keeping the rotor together (the side housing, hence "side ports") or in the curved housing around the rotor (hence "peripheral ports" because they were on the periphery of the rotor).

For three years, from 1954 to 1957, two separate teams worked on different versions of the rotary engine, sharing only the basic shape of the housing and rotor, the sealing system, the four-stroke cycle, and the grinding machine developed by Hoeppner. Yet NSU was in no financial shape to support one daring new technical ven-

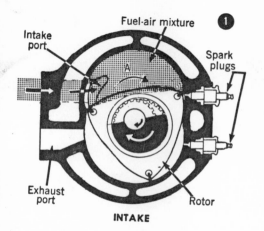

Fuel-air mixture

Intake port

A

Spark plugs

Intake port

Exhaust port

Rotor

INTAKE

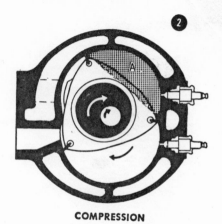

A

COMPRESSION

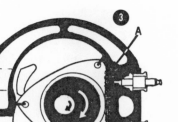

A

A

IGNITION

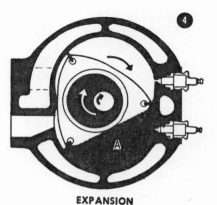

A

EXPANSION

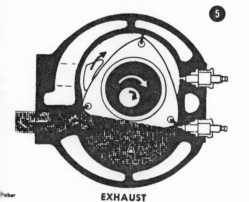

A

EXHAUST

The KKM

The KKM rotary engine has three small chambers of different sizes. Each chamber undergoes a complete four-stroke Otto cycle in one revolution of the rotor.

The five diagrams illustrate what happens in the chamber labeled A.

On the intake stroke a fresh charge of fuel and air enters the chamber through the intake port, which is always open. As the rotor turns clockwise the fuel-air mixture in chamber A is sealed off and compression begins. When the mixture is fully compressed, it is ignited by the firing of the spark plug. The expanding combustion gases drive against the rotor until the exhaust port is uncovered by the movement of the rotor, allowing the spent gases to escape.

ture, let alone two. Sales of its Quickly motorcycles had reached their peak in 1955, and early the next year NSU was stuck with 40,000 unsold units as the market moved toward small cars. These were bad years for companies like NSU, which had thrived on the production of the most basic forms of personal transport. Only fifteen out of the seventy-five firms that had been making motorized cycles in Germany at the beginning of the 1950s survived the decade.

The year 1956 was obviously not going to see the end of NSU's financial problems. The previous year NSU had decided to design and produce a small family car. This was not due to be produced until 1958; in the meantime, NSU was faced with the burden of financing the construction of a new car plant out of the declining proceeds of its motorcycle business. In 1956, NSU had to lay off one-fifth of its 7,500 workers because of declining sales. For months it was unable to raise even the necessary funds to complete the construction of the car plant. Finally, von Heydekampf managed to persuade a reluctant provincial government to lend them the necessary $2.5 million. Von Haydekampf had prudently retained $10 million to start to finance the new venture; as former head of Adam Opel, he alone of the management or the board of directors had any idea of the true capital cost required to produce cars, but even he was not prepared for the savagery of the downturn in business.

Under these circumstances, allotting even an additional $20,000 for the KKM seemed ridiculous. But von Heydekampf got support from an unexpected quarter, one of the two directors nominated to the company's supervisory board by the Dresdner Bank after the war. The first was the chairman, Dr. Richter, known as the "liquidator" because his role for the bank had been to clear up the mess left by incompetent managements. The other, Fritz Vierhub, was a long-serving bank employee who had worked his way up through the ranks, starting as a teen-age clerk. The crucial meeting of the supervisory board was held in an improbable setting: the side of the pool in von Heydekampf's small suburban garden, with the distinguished directors in their bathing trunks, one boiling hot summer's day in 1956. It was the unlikely figure of Vierhub who proposed, in a moment of summer euphoria, that, despite its straitened circumstances, NSU should go ahead with rotary research.

But that was not the last problem. The following year a group of NSU executives on the commercial and personnel sides of the business * rebelled against the money being lavished on the new engine at a time when NSU's financial situation was so insecure. Indeed, they wanted Froede to be sacked. Von Heydekampf was furious and ordered that anyone who interfered with the research in any way would lose his job. As he says of those days, "If I hadn't been an engineer, the whole project would have been killed." But even he would have been helpless if the engine had not worked.

* German companies have two boards of directors: one "managerial," chaired by the chief executive, and responsible for the day-to-day running of the company; the other "supervisory." Apart from the chief executive—who is appointed by the supervisory board—the managerial board consists entirely of nonexecutives representing the interests of the shareholders.

5

The Controversial Cart Horse

"You have made a cart horse out of my race horse."
—FELIX WANKEL

On February 1, 1957, Wankel's own design, the DKM 54, was ready for a trial run under its own power; previously it had been run only as a compressor, relying on compressed air from outside the unit to turn the rotor.

Volatile methanol fuel was used. If the sealing system failed to cope with the high pressures involved, the engine would backfire dangerously. Therefore, only Froede and one of his assistants stayed in the test-cell with the engine. The seals held, the engine started— but ran only spasmodically. The carburetor was soon changed and the jets adjusted. After the changes, the world's first rotary engine ran continuously and sweetly. The next day Wankel himself phoned. Unaware that the engine had run successfully, he warned that no attempt should be made to start it because he had just realized that the whole sealing system was inadequate.

In the next few months, a bigger engine, the DKM 125 (125 cc) was built. It achieved twenty-one horsepower when it was run at 13,000 rpm, and would produce full power for two hours at a time if run at 8,000 rpm. Seals of a different size were then tried. The interior of the inner rotor was hollowed out to improve the cooling, and by the end of the year the engine was producing twenty-six horsepower at 15,000 rpm. Another DKM was tested up to 25,000 rpm in a special safety tunnel. Wankel's theory that his engine would

44

work at speeds far higher than those usual in a reciprocating unit without disintegrating proved to be correct.

But the next year, 1958, was the year of doom for the DKM. On July 1, 1958, a 125-cc KKM engine, based on a discarded design of Wankel's, and weighing only thirty-seven pounds, ran for the first time. Wankel objected strongly: "These young people," he complained, referring to Froede's engineers, "always know better and have ruined my whole plan for a real connecting link between the reciprocating piston engine and the turbine. . . . You have made a cart horse out of my race horse." For Wankel the KKM was a denial of his dream of a purely rotary design that would not require any counterweights or other "artificial" contrivances. Despite Wankel's objections, work on his DKM was suspended by the end of 1958, after only three had been built. The Wankel engine we are familiar with today is, in fact, the rejected offspring of the inventor that was adopted by Froede because of its more immediate practicability.

But using the KKM as the prototype for rotary engine development did not solve all the problems by any means. Proving that the rotary engine worked in principle opened up a hundred questions. What was the best shape for a rotary engine? Should it have one or more rotors? How should you compare it with a reciprocating engine? Would it, in practice, live up to its theoretical promise and be lighter, smoother, quieter, cheaper, and simpler to make and to run than the reciprocating engine?

Even now, seventeen years later, most of these questions are still matters for fierce dispute. But the shape of the engine, one of the most fundamental points of its design, has remained the same. There are, fortunately, only two major variables when deciding on the shape of a rotary engine: the thickness of a rotor compared with its diameter, and the degree of "wobble"—the lurching movement which created the different sizes of chamber. If the rotor and the hollow in each face where combustion actually takes place were too narrow, then the amount of actual combustion capacity for a given size of engine would be much smaller than in a unit that was much fatter, much squatter, and therefore had a very broad rotor. But if the rotor was too wide, then the rate of combustion was too slow and inefficient.

A similar balancing act between two incompatible qualities was required over the lurch, or "eccentricity," of the rotor. For the best possible engine performance, the highest practicable "compression ratio" is required, that is, the difference between the size of the combustion chamber at its biggest and at its smallest. In a rotary engine, this is achieved by increasing the eccentricity and thus the amount by which the rotor lurches around within its housing. The sharper the movement, the bigger the contrast between the minimum and maximum size, the higher the compression ratio, and the greater the efficiency of the engine. But the greater the lurch, the sharper the "angular shift" (the angles endured on every revolution by the apex seals in relation to the housing wall), and the worse the strain on the seals and on the gears which actually transmit the power from the rotor outside the engine. This strain provides a limit for the eccentricity.

The range of the angles between seal and housing used in experimental engines has varied between a mere seven to a massive fifty degrees, but a standard swing of about twenty-five degrees was soon established. This provided a compression ratio of between 7.5 and 10 to 1, similar to that used in an ordinary reciprocating engine.°

Significantly, it proved relatively easy to decide on the shape and eccentricity of the rotor components which had no equivalents in a reciprocating engine, for the engineers working on the rotary had no preconceptions about the rotors themselves. This mental clean slate was, unfortunately, impossible to achieve for tackling the rotary's other problems. Any engineer brought up on reciprocating engines was bound to slip into the habit of thinking of the rotary engine as merely another four-cycle engine in which a fuel-air mixture was ignited by a spark, like the piston engine. The consequent inability to make the necessary leap in imagination to realize that the rotary's apparent similarities with the reciprocating engine concealed much deeper differences has proved most damaging to the rotary's development.

One apparently major advantage the rotary possessed over other challengers to the reciprocating internal-combustion engine was that it followed the same thermodynamic cycle as an ordinary engine and could draw on the accumulated know-how of seventy years in at

---

° In technical rotary language, this eccentricity is expressed as the R/e ratio, the relationship between the radius of the rotor and the degree of eccentricity, or as the K factor. And clearly a low R/e—with a smaller radius compared with the amount the rotor moves from side to side—produces an efficient and, above all, a compact engine.

least two crucial respects—the mixing of gas and air and the ignition of the mixture. Other rivals, like the electric motor, the gas turbine, and even the diesel, require new, expensive, and sometimes exotic accessories.

What are the advantages of a Wankel over a reciprocating internal engine? One advantage is its smoothness and quietness. Most of the noise from a reciprocating unit comes from two factors that are largely absent from a rotary engine: mechanical noise and inherent imbalance. Because a rotary engine has no valves, no valve gear, no connecting rods, none of the clatter and fuss needed to let the gas and air in and out and to translate up-and-down motion to rotary movement, not even its most bitter opponents (who include many of the world's best automotive engineers) can deny that the Wankel is quieter at high speeds. Nor can they deny that the Wankel is balanced. In a V-8 engine, one cylinder from each bank of four is firing at the same time and thus provides a balanced power thrust. But in a four-cylinder unit, the thrust is unbalanced. In a Wankel, every single revolution of the rotor provides three combustion strokes, as the mixture in front of each rotor face is ignited in turn. Power then is being generated smoothly over at least three-quarters of the circle, instead of in a series of jerks, as in the six-cylinder engine.

In a reciprocating engine, the designer is always trying to cram in as many cylinders as possible to achieve a smooth movement and increased piston area (and hence power). In the rotary engine, each triangular rotor is inherently balanced. The obvious thing to do was to employ only one rotor to do the work of four or even six cylinders.

If only one larger rotor is used to do the work of two smaller ones, manufacturing is simpler. There are also fewer problems with sealing. Walter Froede worked out that the total length of line around each chamber that has to be sealed is only two-thirds as long in a one-rotor engine as it would be in a two-rotor engine of the same capacity. Finally, in a single-rotor unit, the surface-to-volume ratio is lower than in a two-rotor unit (in other words, relatively more air can be contained in the given area a housing takes up, thus producing greater efficiency of combustion).

The problem that has prevented the one-rotor engine from becoming a practical proposition in motor vehicles is that the firing impulses are spaced relatively far apart, so the engine can be distinctly heard. The equivalent in an ordinary engine is a four-stroke machine with only two cylinders, or a single-cylinder two-stroke machine (like those used in outboard motors), where each downward stroke produces power.

The noise is considered too great for the one-rotor engine to come into widespread use in modern autos. No wonder William Figart of Curtiss-Wright has declared, "You'll probably never see less than two rotors . . . bècause with one rotor the torque (thrust) can be sensed by the driver." *

Apart from the unit used in the experimental NSU Spyder (see page 92), the single-rotor engine has successfully competed only against the even rougher two-stroke cycle used for outboard motors and snowmobiles. But as the rotary engine gets faster and smoother, a single rotor could well prove to be a practical proposition—already one of General Motors' experimental single-rotor units has proved to be smoother than the very rough four-cylinder reciprocating unit used in the Chevrolet Vega.

At the other extreme, there are considerable mechanical complications if more than three rotors are used to achieve the maximum number of firings and the greatest possible smoothness. At the present time, most rotary motors have two rotors.

The hope ahead for the single-rotor engine can be seen by the fact that in practice (as opposed to mechanical theory), it has often been compared with a four-cylinder, and a two-rotor with a six-cylinder, reciprocating engine. But a more basic comparison between engines is their capacity (i.e., the volume of the combustion chambers, cylinders, or whatever). This has proved more difficult to make, and since the capacity of an engine is used for a variety of purposes (e.g., to decide the amount a car should be taxed or the appropriate class for it in an auto race) the rotary's opponents have seized on the confusion over capacity to make invidious comparisons between it and a reciprocating engine.

It is easy to measure the capacity of a reciprocating engine. You simply take the difference in the volume of the air contained by each cylinder measured where the piston is at the top and then at the

* With a single-rotor Wankel the torque, which measures the thrust or twist delivered by the engine to the transmission, is delivered irregularly. This creates vibrations in the transmission—which are especially noticeable at low speeds—and create the need for a heavy flywheel to smooth out the delivery of the power. In its turn, the weight of the flywheel reduces the liveliness of the engine and the ease and speed with which the gears can be changed.

bottom of a stroke and multiply by the number of cylinders. You can then describe the result either in liters or cubic inches, depending on your continent. Similarly, a Wankel's capacity can be measured. Karl Ludvigsen suggests subtracting "the minimum volume of the chamber—its cubic capacity at the point of greatest compression—from the maximum volume the chamber reaches as the rotor revolves. The space that's left represents the chamber's pumping capacity, its theoretical ability to breathe and process an air-fuel mixture." That works, but a further question immediately arises: Is a rotor one cylinder or more? For every revolution of the motor, the engine fires three times; thus the first inclination was to multiply the volume of each chamber by three—so the KKM 125 became a 375-cc engine (3 × 125 cc). But in practice this would obviously be unfair, because the output shaft (as opposed to the rotor) goes around once for every power stroke because of the gearing between the rotor and the shaft. Counting each rotor as one cylinder would obviously help the Wankel enormously by placing it in a lower class for taxation or racing purposes.

In the end, a meaningless compromise has been reached. Groups such as the international motor racing authorities and Swiss car tax collectors double the volume of a single Wankel chamber to produce a capacity figure. This multiple was not decided until after a heated argument, in which leading engineering authorities were called in to prove, successively, that the Wankel resembled either a two-stroke engine or a two-cylinder four-stroke engine. Today the argument still continues. Karl Ludvigsen himself believes that the Wankel's true size is three times the volume of a single chamber and uses this larger size when explaining the great development potential of the Wankel.

Many rotary enthusiasts feel that this compromise formula devised by these international bodies in the 1960s is unfair to the Wankel. Certainly the "antirotarians" running international motor racing in the early 1960s used the formula to hamstring rotary cars in manufacturers' efforts to prove rotaries on the world's racetracks. For example, Porsche had been developing a rotary engine for racing use, but abandoned the option it had on a license once the double-volume formula had been adopted. In another case, Toyo Kogyo of Japan claimed that one of its rotary engines had a volume of less than 360 cc (engines of this size are accorded favorable tax treatment in

Japan). But when the formula was devised, antirotarians in Toyo Kogyo's rival companies were able to use it to sabotage the attempt to gain the tax relief.

In theory, of course, a rotary engine should be smaller and lighter than a reciprocating unit of comparable power. Indeed, Wankel's early work had been encouraged and subsidized because even rotary valves offered such an advantage in compactness. How much greater, therefore, the possibilities inherent in a rotary engine?

The claims have often been extravagant. Jan Norbye, author of the leading technical work on the engine, claims that it is "half the weight of a reciprocating engine of comparable output." At the height of the Wankel boom in the United States, *Fortune* magazine said, "It has forty percent fewer parts, weighs anything from a third to half as much and is half the size."

In fact, it is easy to rig the argument either way, depending on which engine is compared with the Wankel. A reciprocating engine designed twenty years ago makes a Wankel, in contrast, look light and compact. Choose a more modern orthodox unit and the contrast is more doubtful—for the art of designing reciprocating engines has advanced considerably since the arrival of the rotary. Graham Bannock, a brilliant British automotive economist, has shown how in the past twenty years engine power has increased by between 50 and 100 percent for units of equal capacity--and in some cases the modern, infinitely more powerful, unit is lighter as well.

The most thorough comparison of reciprocating and rotary engines was carried out by Karl Ludvigsen and shows clearly why the major European motor manufacturers have not gone overboard for the Wankel. Modern small units—under seventy-five brake horsepower (bhp)—are now so compact that there is no real advantage to the present generation of rotary engines. Seventy-five brake horsepower is the size of many small European family cars, in which an orthodox engine can be tucked away neatly enough. It is then dwarfed by gear boxes, air filters, starter motors, and other accessories common to both rotary and reciprocating engines. Significant advantages of a rotary engine only begin to show up for units of greater horsepower—above 125 bhp, the top limit for the majority of normal-sized European family cars. Only Swedish Volvo and Daimler-Benz among European car manufacturers have a range of vehicles the majority of which have engines producing more than

100 bhp. To invest heavily in an entirely new kind of engine with all its attendant risks, for use in only a few models, would not make obvious sense to, say, Fiat, or Renault, or British Leyland. Only if and when the single-rotor engine becomes a practical proposition would the weight-size comparison be radically transformed, enabling the rotary to compete successfully with the reciprocating engines producing under 100 bhp.

For most American car manufacturers (and Daimler-Benz), the situation is reversed. In terms of weight and size for units producing more than 100 bhp, the advantages of the rotary are considerable. For a 200-bhp unit used in the majority of American vehicles, a Wankel will weigh at least ten percent less than a comparable reciprocating engine. This means a difference of sixty pounds of metal in the engine alone, as well as the reduced weight of the structure required to carry it. The rotor engine will also be nearly a third less bulky, enabling automotive engineers to design smaller and more compact vehicles. Even in cars where the rotary takes up as much space as an orthodox engine would, a rotary is much more compact, with less wasted space.

If its relative size, weight, and shape are theoretical advantages to the Wankel engine, its final claim to superiority is its simplicity. On a Wankel, only the rotor, the internal gearing, and drive shaft move. Because there are so few moving parts in the Wankel, it should be an easier engine to produce. Proponents never tire of laying out for the photographer the multiplicity of parts needed for an ordinary engine, in contrast to the number needed for their beloved rotary. But they ignore the problem of "technological density." This is a phrase of Kenichi Yamamoto of Toyo Kogyo, one of the major figures in rotary development, and summarizes the point that the number of parts is less important than their individual complexity. This complexity involves what the required materials are, the quantity and quality of machined surfaces, tolerances, surface treatments, and design complexity. By these criteria, the rotary has so far scored badly against the reciprocating engine, whose parts are made out of simple, cheap materials and can be stamped out easily in tens of millions. Many of the parts and processes involved in the production of the rotary engine have become even more complicated and are, at least at first, expensive to produce. We have already noted the problem, which was to be a recurring one, of producing and finishing the rotor housing. The apex seals on the rotor have also undergone many changes. One design of apex seal contains fifty-eight parts; each of these is made to very exact tolerances, or is of expensive and sometimes exotic materials.

"Technological density" also applies to the time needed to manufacture an engine. Walter Froede once estimated that whereas a rotary had only a marginal advantage when it came to the cost of materials, it should only require half the time of man- and machinery-hours to manufacture as an orthodox engine. But even this has not yet been proved, simply because fewer than a million rotary engines have been produced so far. There is still something of a vicious circle: The Wankel is too expensive to produce because no one makes it in a sufficient quantity to cut its production costs; because no one company is producing enough rotary engines, it is considered objectively more expensive.

Finally, at the bottom of the balance sheet, comes fuel consumption—the item which has done more to harm the engine's reputation recently than anything else. This is a function of the present stage of development of the engine—the trade-off required between fuel consumption and durability. But it will not be a permanent factor. Even if it were, the rotary's greater gas consumption should not matter too much in an ideal world since it can use much cruder fuel than that required by an orthodox engine, well below ninety-one octane, the lowest on sale in many developed countries. If the rotary had only got there first, no oil company would now be prepared to refine gasoline above seventy-five or eighty octane. As it is, they are not going to spend vast sums of money to refine and distribute a cheaper product than their present range of ninety-one to ninety-nine octane unless the automobile manufacturers or the public insist on it.

But whatever the balance sheet we can now draw up, twenty years after the engine was invented, the advantages of the rotary engine did not seem very compelling at the time it first started to work. In the words of NSU's chairman, Dr. Richter, what was needed in 1954 was an "icebreaker," a large company that would show its faith in the engine—and share in the onerous development costs.

6

The Hard Sell

"Inventors are people who respect neither law nor order and
have usually already ruined their families."

—ERNST HUTZENLAUB

The arguments about the exact point at which a rotary engine
becomes a serious economic proposition seemed very remote when
von Heydekampf went out to look for partners who would take out
licenses or share in development costs. Even before the DKM
worked as an engine for the first time, he had hawked the engine to
virtually the whole of the German vehicle industry, with no success.
Personally, he was a well-known and respected figure, but his company was then by no means sound, and the idea was considered
merely a personal foible. Even executives who knew personally of
Wankel's work were not necessarily in favor of developing his ideas.
As one put it, "He is one of those inventors who are far too preoc-
cupied with their own ideas [instead of their commercial
application]."

But before any rights could be peddled, Wankel and NSU had to
clear up the patent situation—and regularize Wankel's own relationship with other companies, in particular, Goetze and Borsig.

Wankel had already used the alleged existence of a contract with
Borsig to help persuade NSU to back his rotary ideas. At the time,
there was, in fact, no such contract. (Borsig only sent Wankel a draft
agreement in June 1954, six months after he had claimed it was
already in force; in fact, he never signed it at all.) But Wankel clearly
hoped that Borsig would develop and build a rotary compressor well
before NSU achieved the much more difficult job of producing a
rotary engine. In fact, as von Heydekampf realized, there were
hundreds of configurations for a rotary compressor already in exist-

53

ence; so Wankel's idea on this was by no means unique, as it obviously could be for an engine. With this in mind, NSU was prepared to let Borsig have all the rights for the use of the Wankel principle in compressors. After some acrimonious correspondence, the two companies got together; even when NSU discovered that Borsig had no legal rights to the idea because there was no contract in existence, it let the rights for compressor use go. So far, von Heydekampf has been proved right: Not a single compressor using Wankel's configuration has yet come on the market.

The patent situation had been clarified to some extent even before the engine actually worked. Three basic patents were applied for: by Wankel alone covering the shape of the housing; by Wankel and Hoeppner covering the gas flow in the engine—it had been Hoeppner's idea to route the incoming gas through the center shaft in the DKM; and by Wankel, Hoeppner, and Froede covering the sealing system. The only major objection was overcome by a generous personal gesture almost unique in the whole story. For, in 1943, eleven years before Wankel, a Swiss engineer, Bernard Maillard, working for the truck builders Adolph Saurer, had patented the same configuration—the triangular rotor in a peanut-shaped housing—but had placed the seals on the housing at the narrow waist of the housing, not, as had Wankel, on the tips of the rotor. As a result, his idea did not naturally provide a four-stage combustion cycle. Because of this difference, Maillard voluntarily gave up in advance any claims he might have had to share in the patent rights. This gesture "gave us the chance of building up a real patent structure," in the words of von Heydekampf.

Thanks to Maillard's attitude, models of the engine were shown to the Patent Office in Munich at the end of January 1955, and the patents were granted. In the next three years, NSU and Wankel registered at least thirty more patents, a policy designed to plant a minefield around the basic patents and ensure that no one else could block their exclusive rights to this type of engine. They were so successful that anyone wanting to make a rotary engine has had to negotiate with Wankel and NSU ever since. The best testimony to the watertightness of the basic patent structure—at least until the end of the 1970s, when they expire—is that even General Motors felt obliged to buy a license to enable it to build Wankel engines.

Wankel and NSU then had to come to some agreement over their respective shares of the future spoils. This introduced to the story two middlemen, Peter Lindenmayr and Ernst Hutzenlaub, who between them assured Wankel's position. While Hutzenlaub is still active, having made at least $20 million from the engine, Lindenmayr has retired and completely disappeared from the rotary scene. His signature, an illegible scrawl, stands at the foot of some of the key contracts in the story, but his name is unknown to most of the people who have been developing the engine in recent years and forgotten even by pioneers like von Heydekampf.

Lindenmayr was apparently one of the engineers on the German wartime rocket program who went to the United States after the war to work with Wernher von Braun. In the middle of the 1950s, Lindenmayr was the European representative for the American aeroengine company of Curtiss-Wright. At the end of 1956, he appeared at Neckarsulm, saying that he had heard about the Wankel engine from Professor Huber of Munich. And, in March the next year, he was the first outsider to see the engine in action—NSU used to demonstrate the DKM by letting it roll around the floor of the workshop under its own power because, of course, on the DKM the outer casing as well as the rotor revolved.

Lindenmayr was deeply impressed and tried to persuade Roy Hurley, then chairman of Curtiss-Wright, of the engine's virtues, but Hurley was not impressed. He thought the engine sounded too good to be true. He then sent Karl Lundqvist, his chief engineer, over to look at the engine, but Lundqvist had his own ideal engine he wanted Hurley to develop and therefore sent him a discouraging report on the Wankel. Lindenmayr then resigned his job with Curtiss-Wright in disgust (though another account says that he was sacked) and went to work for Wankel, first as his personal representative, then, in 1958, as the managing director of Wankel G.m.B.h., the private company he formed to take care of any profits he might make from his inventions. Even before the first engine had run, Wankel had drawn up an organizational chart of a joint development club, which included Daimler-Benz, Borsig, and Germany's prestigious Fraunhofer Engineering Foundation as well as NSU. Sensibly enough, in view of NSU's precarious situation, Wankel wanted to spread the risk and ensure that one person's—or one company's—cold feet could not kill his idea.

But first there had to be some agreement with NSU over the

division of any royalties or license fees from the engine. Normally an employee could expect only a small percentage of any such profits, but Wankel was no ordinary worker, even though he had a contract with NSU giving the firm the rights to the results of his work. But the possibility of any real windfall seemed remote; von Heydekampf did not want to be accused of living off some poor inventor's blood, and most of the NSU board were prepared to offer Wankel a twenty-four-percent stake, a carefully chosen percentage, one below the level at which a minority shareholder acquires some important rights under German law; a shareholder with twenty-five percent has the right to block increases in capital, changes in the board, and most other consequential changes in the "company structure."

As so often at critical points in his life, Wankel relied on help from Keppler, who suggested that Dr. Voss, an independent arbitrator, should be brought in. Wankel applied further pressure by claiming that he had some new technical ideas that would be valuable for developing the engine; after which direct negotiations started in earnest.

Wankel, Lindenmayr, and von Heydekampf finally settled a deal in a small restaurant near the NSU factory. At first Wankel, prompted by Lindenmayr, asked for fifty percent of the profits, claiming that he was entitled in fact to more than half, but would settle at that figure. Von Heydekampf offered thirty-five percent, and they eventually settled on forty percent, with the proviso that Wankel would take on a forty-percent share of the research and development work. NSU's then patent lawyer, Herr Tetzner, was cynical about Wankel's further usefulness: "He has laid his big egg," he remarked of Wankel. "He will not lay another." And in fact Wankel contributed virtually nothing further to the development of the engine he had sired. His hostile attitude to NSU also seems to date from the agreement.

This was partly his own nature; Wankel has been less interested in the application of his ideas than in his next project. He has tended to be impatient, to want to move on always to new ones. In addition, the engine NSU was developing was not one he totally approved of—a child of his certainly, but by no means his favorite son (though, quite naturally, he resists the notion that it was Froede's own idea). And there was one other curious psychological point: Wankel was always deeply disappointed that his creation had been taken up, not by the mighty and technically respected firm of Daimler-Benz, but by a relatively obscure motorcycle company. This disappointment carried through to the time when General Motors took out their license. The terms made him substantially richer, but, like many staunch German nationalists, he was always anti-American, and therefore doubly disappointed that his idea would only be fully exploited in the United States.

One person who did take seriously the obligation to help further with the research on the engine was Ernst Hutzenlaub, whom Lindenmayr introduced to Wankel. Hutzenlaub bought a half share in Wankel's company, and then, armed with the rights negotiated by Lindenmayr, went on to make both Wankel and himself millionaires several times over. Lindenmayr was less lucky; shortly after he had been appointed manager of Wankel's private company, Hutzenlaub and Wankel succeeded in having him removed, leaving Hutzenlaub triumphant.

Hutzenlaub is one of the most controversial characters in the whole history of the engine. He started (but did not complete) training as an architect. After the war, he married the daughter of the owner of a rubber company, Gummi Muller, and quickly grasped how much money could be made from selling the licenses for patents. He also learned how to reduce his tax bill in Germany by ensuring that income from outside the country derived from his patents was channeled through Switzerland, thus gaining him the benefit of tax concessions designed by the German government to encourage the exploitation abroad of German inventions.

Hutzenlaub is a big, heavy, and energetic man who, despite the $20 million he has made from the Wankel alone, still travels 60,000 miles a year rushing around Europe in a $20,000 Maserati Ghibli sports car looking for new patents to exploit. He also has a staff of 200 looking at new ideas—about one in fifty of which they find have any potential. If he takes them up, he gets half of the income, as he did with Wankel, for helping to develop and sell the ideas. Although he makes his money from helping inventors, he is cynical about them. They are, he says, "people who respect neither law nor order and have usually already ruined their families."

Hutzenlaub's role in the Wankel development has been largely as a middleman and negotiator (though he did take seriously the commitment to undertake further research on the engine, using for the purpose a workshop belonging to the Rex motorcycle company which belonged to him).

Hutzenlaub is a very persuasive salesman; although, for instance, he is not a trained engineer, he became so involved with the Wankel engine that it was a whole year before even von Heydekampf's trained eye spotted that he was a layman.

However, not even Hutzenlaub's persuasive tongue was enough to bring off his first attempt to raise more funds for the engine. Lindenmayr and Hutzenlaub tried to arrange for help from a certain Mr. Newman, a British-born war surplus and arms dealer who lived in Paris. In the summer of 1957, Newman offered an interest-free loan of up to $500,000 to enable NSU to produce a prototype engine within a couple of years. In return, Newman would have an option for licenses in France, Scandinavia, the Low Countries (Benelux), and possibly other European countries such as Italy. He was not interested in doing business in Germany or Britain because, he said, their taxes were immorally high. Never interested in the engine as such, Newman made it perfectly clear when he met von Heydekampf later that year that he did not care if the business in question "concerned engines or potatoes," so long as it made money. NSU turned down his offer.

But Hutzenlaub's talents did succeed in tidying up another loose end. Goetze, the piston ring manufacturer, still retained the rights to develop the ideas which Wankel had given it when, in the early 1950s, he had sold the rights to his ideas simultaneously to several companies, a time when, as NSU says, "he was being polygamous although married to us." Thanks to the tact of Ernst Fuhrmann, then in charge of Goetze's development program, and Hutzenlaub's negotiating skill, a compromise was reached. Goetze agreed to give up its rights to the engine, in return for a guarantee that all orders for the components needed to seal Wankel engines would go through Goetze (which was not a very big concession, since it was Germany's leading manufacturer of engines and gas seals and would almost certainly have got the orders anyway).

But the more productive work of actually finding another firm to take an interest in the engine went badly. Borsig, Porsche, Alfa-Romeo, and Volkswagen formed a roll call of visitors, all famous, all unimpressed—especially by the fact that the engine could not be started at less than 2,000 rpm. Professor Nallinger, the head of

Daimler-Benz's technical developments, had allegedly promised to help with $150,000, but the money never materialized.

Abroad von Heydekampf himself took the engine to Volvo and Saab in Sweden, with no success. A close friend of his, an industrial banker called Max Bunford who had a substantial shareholding in NSU, started negotiations with a number of French auto companies. Bunford, who was no engineer, was therefore even more enthusiastic about the engine's virtues than the experts, but when he explained that he was selling an engine, he was told, "You are not selling an engine, you are selling an idea."

The air of suspicion which surrounded the engine at that point was demonstrated during an examination by a representative of the French Aircraft Research Institute. He insisted that the engine be dismantled after the demonstration to ensure that it was indeed a rotary. After chatting for a moment with Frankenberger, he returned to the engine and felt the dismantled parts to make sure they were still hot and there had been no substitution of any sort while he was not looking.

In such an atmosphere, there was not much hope for the engine. NSU was itself distracted by the problem of trying to get their first car, the Prinz, ready for launching in 1958. Then, early that year, quite by chance, Curtiss-Wright and its extraordinary chairman, Roy Hurley, came back onto the scene.

7

Hurley

"Some people say I'm a crook; others say I'm a genius. I guess I'm a mixture of both."

        —Roy "Pat" Hurley, chairman of Curtiss-Wright

Roy Hurley—universally known as "Pat"—was a tough, self-taught automobile engineer and had worked for Ford before he was chosen to head Curtiss-Wright. He lived for his work: "We had to give him something to think about," recalls one former employee, "something to do over Christmas, or Easter, or any other long weekend."

He was autocratic, "hated, but also respected," by those who worked for him. He tended to surround himself with associates from his automobile days, who were not disposed to argue with him. Sixty years old at the end of the 1950s, he liked to think of himself as still young and had married his former secretary, who was considerably younger than he was.

In 1958 he had been chief executive of Curtiss-Wright for nine years, and the ambitions he nourished for the company had spread into areas other than its historic business, the manufacture of aircraft engines. His dream was to develop a company that would not only be a "General Motors of the air," but a major pioneer in surface transport as well.

The Wright stands for the brothers Orville and Wilbur, and the Curtiss for Glenn Curtiss, who sold the first airplane to the U.S. Navy and the second to the U.S. Army. Their two companies had merged just before the great stock market crash of 1929, and during World War II and the Korean War, Curtiss-Wright had become one of the biggest suppliers of aircraft engines to the Pentagon. But it missed out on the early days of development of the jet, relying instead on

60

improved and more complicated versions of propeller units, notably a supercharged unit called the "turbo-compound" engine. This was installed in the DC-7, the last of the prejet airliners.

Hurley's grandiose plans for Curtiss-Wright made him neglect the company's relations with the Defense Department, which had been its fortune before his arrival. The Pentagon wanted the company to plow back into research the profits it had made from the Korean War. Instead, Hurley used the money to buy control of Studebaker-Packard and lavished money on a variety of other unconnected and apparently wacky notions. For example, he was working on a substitute for asphalt based on coal, which, used on aircraft runways, would allegedly stand the strain of the new jet airliners—and jet fuel—better than ordinary asphalt. He tried to turn railroad trains into miniature airliners-on-tracks by adapting the turbo-compound engine to power them. He hoped to develop a train that could travel coast to coast in under twenty-four hours. Simultaneously, Hurley was trying to catch up on the company's previous neglect of jet engines. He unsuccessfully proposed a 10,000-pound unit to power a projected Douglas short-haul airliner, which eventually became the DC-9.

Some of his outlandish ideas were, in fact, intelligent anticipations of future requirements. He was developing a suppressor for jet whine and an "air car" like a hovercraft, which hovered on a cushion of air six to twelve inches above the ground. This actually "flew" in 1959. (One observer recalled how the whoosh of air lifted all the girls' skirts.) He also proposed, again well before its time, to build a vertical takeoff and landing aircraft. For these ideas he was ridiculed. And, although he clearly foresaw some real future needs, if his reign at Curtiss-Wright is judged by orthodox business standards, it was a disaster. Apart from the highly lucrative sales of spare parts for the thousands of Curtiss-Wright engines still in service around the world, he could not find any stable sources of immediate income to pay for the new projects he was always dreaming up and pursuing with such undiscriminating energy.

His second introduction to the Wankel came when William Hannaway, Curtiss-Wright's corporate counsel, visited Munich on behalf of its Studebaker-Packard subsidiary to negotiate a contract with Kugelfischer, a leading manufacturer of carburetors and fuel injection equipment.

Kugelfischer knew of Curtiss-Wright's interest in new power units and told Hannaway about the Wankel. At the time NSU was still free with its secrets; so Hannaway had no difficulty in obtaining an engine, which he duly brought back for Hurley to examine.

Hurley called in Max Bentele, his senior development engineer, one Friday afternoon in May 1958, pointed to the Wankel and said, "This is supposed to be an engine." He asked Bentele to take it away, study it over the weekend, and tell Hurley on Monday whether the idea was worth pursuing. Bentele's presence at Curtiss-Wright and the fact that Hurley chose him to appraise the engine were major strokes of luck. Bentele (the Americans pronounce the name Bentley, the Germans to rhyme with steely) had been one of the pioneers of jet-engine technology in Germany. After the war and a spell of working for C. A. Parsons, a firm of British turbine manufacturers, he was invited to go to Curtiss-Wright, which had heard of him through their chief engineer who had interrogated him after the war.

Despite the language difficulty ("I had to strain myself to understand the American slang," he remembers), Bentele was put in charge of developing mechanical components of all sorts at Curtiss-Wright, in Woodridge, New Jersey. Bentele, a charming man as well as a brilliant engineer, was the first technically qualified outsider to examine the Wankel engine with any real sympathy or understanding. (This attitude was not extended indiscriminately to all rotary engines; he said of the Karol Anidyne, another new rotary engine, that "a description of it should be placed under the headline Show Business in *Time* magazine rather than in the scientific section.")

Over that May weekend, he took the Wankel engine apart, "and I had great difficulty in putting it together again," he says. Bentele immediately grasped the engine's strong points—the natural four-stroke cycle, the absence of valves—and the problems: cooling and, above all, the wear on the seals. On Monday, when he reported to Hurley, he was told for the first time who had designed and built the unit. This somewhat reassured Bentele, who remembered Wankel's wartime work on the sealing problems of aircraft engines; he advised Hurley to take out an option, build some prototypes, and only then decide if it was worth taking out a license. But Hurley, impatient as usual, would not wait. The cost of a license, he said, would be that much greater if there was any delay.

In one way Hurley was right. "At that stage," recalls one observer, "a great deal could be left to the imagination; so it was reasonable to gamble on a tremendous scale." In an unpublished letter to *Fortune* magazine written following a glowing account of the engine in the magazine, Bentele himself put the risk as it appeared in the summer of 1958 in rather more somber fashion:

The engine had been and was being peddled to big and small companies, but not one would spend a nickel on it. There was no basic patent in the United States, and the chances to get one were considered slim. The proposed gas sealing, the major problem of any rotary engine, was a nightmare to design, manufacture, and to assemble, and it was too fragile to last.

The U.S. patent situation was even worse than Bentele indicated. Although there had been relatively few problems in Europe, the lawyer used by NSU had no experience of U.S. patents. He had presented the evidence badly and, above all, had omitted to mention that gears were used to produce a three-to-two ratio between the rotor and the casing—referring, of course, to the DKM. Without the difference in speed between the two, the engine would not work. So the U.S. authorities turned the engine down as unworkable. This sort of "final rejection" really is the end of the road in ninety-nine percent of cases. But Wankel insisted that the lawyer be replaced, and Froede, Lindenmayr, and two new lawyers went to see what they could do to reverse the decision—over what was probably the most basic patent of all, that covering the actual trochoid shape of the housing. Froede had built an engine without gears on which the inner and outer units slid freely. This produced enough compression for the engine to work, and his appeal to the authorities in Washington was successful, against all the odds.

But the appeal was still outstanding when Hurley started to negotiate, following a visit to NSU by Hannaway and Bentele, who came armed with five pages of questions. Hurley's first offer was a mere $50,000, which, despite the pressure from the pessimistic Dresdner Bank, which advised him to take what he could get, prompted von Heydekampf to retort: "Sorry, but we don't take tips."

But the reversal of the U.S. patent position changed the relative bargaining strengths completely, and on October 21, 1958, von

Heydekampf, Hurley, and Lindenmayr signed an agreement by which Curtiss-Wright was to pay a total of $2 million—$750,000 down and the rest over a period of years—for certain specified rights to the engine.

For its money Curtiss-Wright bought an exclusive license for the engine in the United States, and a nonexclusive license throughout the rest of the world, apart from Germany, meaning it could make and sell engines anywhere it wanted. It could, with NSU's permission, make and sell rotary aircraft engines even in Germany. It could issue sublicenses in the United States, but if a license were issued to manufacturers of autos or motorcycles, it would, again, require NSU's permission. Both sides were to get a sliding scale of royalties on the engines made by Curtiss-Wright or one of its licensees. And to encourage Curtiss-Wright actually to produce engines, there would be a minimum payment of $100,000 a year after 1964, when Curtiss-Wright was to cease to have the exclusive American rights.

Even before the agreement was signed, Hurley was impatient to start work. In September, after the summer holidays, and a month before the agreement was signed, Hurley had set Bentele to work. He was allocated a small white hut (nicknamed the "White House"). He asked for one engineer to help him—Charles Jones, then head of Curtiss-Wright's research into stress and applied mechanics, who had done some of the theoretical calculations for Bentele earlier that year. In strictest secrecy—only Jones, Bentele, and their secretary were allowed into the "White House"—they set out to analyze the engine from first principles. For Bentele felt strongly that Froede and his team at NSU had worked too empirically. Therefore, he and Jones decided to work out mathematically the forces and stresses involved in the engine and, proceeding from that diagnosis, to remedy the underlying problems they found. Because of the difference of approach, their relations with the NSU team were not completely harmonious. When Froede asked what replacement parts they wanted for a KKM 125 which had failed under test, Jones replied simply, "Everything except the spark plug wire."

Bentele and Jones persuaded Froede to give up further experiments on the DKM, and that winter, they provided a framework for a new generation of Wankel engines. Whereas Froede "had made it as close to a piston engine as possible," Bentele and Jones could and did treat it as a totally new type of motor whose problems would require very different solutions to those employed in orthodox engines.

Their major problem was lack of time. For Hurley was always in a hurry—when Bentele told him that it would take up to eight years to design an engine suitable for motor cars, Hurley nearly fired him on the spot; within a couple of months Hurley had taken forty-five of Curtiss-Wright's best engineers away from their regular duties and put them to work on the engine. He threw himself into the rotary research game and would turn up at the test stand most mornings at seven o'clock supervising the work. He would make sudden technical decisions, say, on changing the spark plugs, and there would immediately be a chorus of "Yes, let's change the spark plugs" from the cronies who surrounded him. When an engine ran for an unprecedented 1,000 hours, there was, inevitably, a champagne party.

With—or in spite of—Hurley's help, Bentele and Jones accomplished an amazing amount that winter, culminating in the design and production within six months of a much more refined unit than anything the Germans had yet produced, followed soon afterward by the RC 1-60 (rotating combustion, one rotor, sixty cubic inches, or eight times the volume of the basic NSU 125-cc unit). The two-rotor version of this, naturally named the RC 2-60, was to provide Curtiss-Wright with their basic test rig for a decade or more to come.

But Hurley's plans extended far beyond the manufacture of one type of engine. Even before the first one-rotor engine was working, he was telling Bentele to design one with four rotors. He dreamed, naturally, of rotary aircraft engines; he conceived an idea for putting a massive rotary unit in a truck. Since, he reasoned, you could pack more Wankel power into the maximum size of truck the law permitted, a rotary-powered vehicle would be powerful enough to tackle the Rockies much faster, thus saving at least a day on the coast-to-coast haul. He had, however, one extremely shrewd and practical thought. He saw clearly that the ideal showpiece vehicle for the engine would not be a worthy, if useful, truck, but a glamorous leisure vehicle whose purchasers, concerned above all with fashion, would overlook the inevitably high price required of them and would not worry if their repair bills were on the high side. He proposed, therefore, to put one of the early engines into a fast speedboat to be marketed in limited numbers as a status symbol.

For these dreams he needed, not just one engine, but a whole range. Bentele and Jones duly produced ten or more. They made the RC 1-4.3, a tiny air-cooled unit, constructed largely of aluminum and weighing only twenty-five pounds, suitable for lawn mowers and chain saws. It was deliberately designed to perform its task "just well enough." It was not an ideal engine, but one that could be produced at a competitive price. Indeed, when its potential cost was added up, the theory that a rotary was not inherently more expensive than an orthodox engine seemed proved.

At the other end of the scale, they produced a monstrous great engine, as big as a man, the RC 1-1920, which still stands outside Jones's office. The RC 1-1920 was designed to produce 1,000 hp, but it was discovered that the flame just could not travel fast enough down its monstrous great chambers to ignite all the mixture effectively, and before it was abandoned, it had produced a maximum power of under 800 bhp.

But Bentele and Jones will be remembered, not for the exotic engines they produced, but for the more fundamental work they did on the engine in the four years after September 1958. In that time they found solutions to some of the most basic problems afflicting the engine. The first was cooling, especially of the curved housing round the rotor. In an ordinary reciprocating engine, each cylinder is cooled regularly by the fresh incoming charges of gas and air, and no part of the engine has worse cooling problems than any other. But with a rotary engine, the fresh, cool charge enters the chamber at the same point on the clock, as it were, on each revolution, and since the spark plug is also fixed at one point on the housing, combustion takes place at the same place every time. This creates a permanently cool side to the engine and a permanently hot one. NSU followed automotive practice, adopted "circumferential cooling" so that the cooling water circulated only around the housing, not within it. Bentele and Jones analyzed the flow of heat through the engine and turned the housing into a honeycomb to allow water to be forced through it. The wall of the rotor housing was made thinner near the hotter areas to allow the heat to escape more freely. Their "stitched flow" cooling system more or less solved the housing cooling problem, and their method has been used ever since (small rotary engines, or those for aircraft, can be air-cooled, in which case they have long cooling vanes on the hot side and shorter ones, or none at all, on the cool side).

Even more fundamental work was required on the seals. The first they tackled was not on the apex seals but those on the side of the rotor. Wankel and Froede had both used thin plates for this purpose, but these could not adjust to the great changes in temperatures involved. So Bentele fitted curved strips of metal similar to those used for the apex seals. These then evolved, as described by another Curtiss-Wright engineer, William Figart:

> Engines speak to you if only you'd listen. If you run an engine and it breaks down, it will tell you where something went wrong. At one point we were noticing excessive wear on the little retaining pin that holds the side seals in their grooves. What the engine was saying was, "Lighter, lighter, make the side seals lighter." The side seals were rather heavy then—they were about ¼ inch in cross section, and you would have thought they were just fine. But they were just too heavy and too rigid, and they were causing wear on the housing. So we switched to lighter weight, more flexible seals, and that took care of that.

The apex seals—for nearly a decade the heart of the engine's troubles—were another matter. When Curtiss-Wright started working on the engine, "the seals had very short lifetimes. They'd last only for seconds, a minute if we were lucky." The problem was particularly acute at the corners, where they had to fit into the retaining pin which joined them to the side seals. When Bentele and Jones started work on the engine, these corners had two thin pieces of metal to fix into a slot that was itself only 90/1,000th of an inch thick—less than a tenth of an inch in which to fit a corner piece which itself had a slit in the middle in which was fitted a thin metal wafer. This was only 20/1,000th of an inch thick and quite unable to sustain the pressures involved for any length of time. Bentele and Jones first fitted a solid corner seal, backed by a leaf spring (which operated only when the engine started; once it had gathered speed, the gas itself provided the necessary pressure, as Wankel always thought it would). Even this proved troublesome; for any apex seal had to be short enough to get through the cold side, which is the narrowest part of the housing. Since the housing is wider on its hotter side (the metal in the housing shrinks at the colder point), the seal was not large enough at that point and leaked at the corner. This leak is not important at high speeds. It *was* at low revolutions. Eventually Jones patented a double seal, with a triangular-shaped wedge at the corners.

After reconstructing the seals, Curtiss-Wright went to look for better, tougher materials with which to make them. They invited the chairman and chief engineer of Perfect Circle, a major manufacturer of piston rings, to come and help. "They were sworn to secrecy," Bentele remembers, "on a stack of bibles." But the chief engineer remembered the engine well, for he had seen it a year before on a visit to Volvo in Sweden. At that point, a year after Curtiss-Wright had acquired the license, Hurley decided that there was no point in trying to hide the engine any longer. On November 12, 1959, the first hints appeared of a revolutionary new engine to be revealed by Curtiss-Wright during the week of November 23.

On that day, Hurley took full-page advertisements to announce the arrival of his wonder engine. The press were shown an outline of the engine and a film of it in action. According to one report, the display included "one engine not much larger than a pumpkin . . . shown in action pumping water for five fire hoses—yet it was working below full power." Hurley was reported as claiming that the engine "had only two moving parts . . . and was two to four times the power of a piston engine of the same weight . . . you can stack them up like pancakes . . . they have a wide variety of uses." The only limit Hurley would admit was that the engine was not competitive with big jet engines (even though a "unit in the 750 to 5,000 hp class is also under development").

Hurley's imagination reached its finest flowering in listing the range of uses to which the engine could be put:

Curtiss-Wright had directed its efforts to providing power plants in all fields of transportation, including automotive, marine, commercial aircraft, and vertical takeoff aircraft with ranges up to 1,000 miles.

In addition, the press release continued:

Because of its compactness and low weight, there will be a wide application in the industrial equipment field covering compressors, generators, pumps, farm implements, and earth-moving equipment.

Curtiss-Wright had explained at the top of the press release that the engine "had been developed jointly with NSU Werke, of West Germany." But the name of the man usually thought of as the engine's inventor occurred only in the last sentence. Almost as an afterthought, the release concluded:

Felix Wankel, associated with NSU Werke, invented the principle from which the present engine has been developed.

Hurley was asking for trouble. Hurley's showmanship, enthusiasm—and total lack of tact—first of all created major and immediate problems. The first was with the Securities and Exchange Commission (SEC). After the reports on the engine had appeared in the papers on Tuesday, November 24, Curtiss-Wright stock took off. On the Tuesday it was up over $3 to $35.25. On the Wednesday the opening was delayed by heavy buying orders. Eventually, it opened at $38 and was up over the $40 mark by the end of the day. But after trading had finished, Hurley announced some bad financial results for the third quarter and a cut in the quarterly dividend from 62½¢ to 37½¢. On Thursday the stock dropped back below the $40 mark, was suspended, opened again at $36.50, and eventually closed below $35, having been "far and away the most actively traded stock" that day. Not surprisingly, the head of the New York office of the SEC hauled Hurley before him to "explain the sequence of corporate events which I thought warranted an investigation." The truth was not obvious—that Hurley's ill-timed enthusiasm for the engine was just that, and not, as a cynical SEC official might have assumed, an elaborate smoke screen designed to divert attention from Curtiss-Wright's underlying financial problems. In fact, the investigation petered out, and no action was taken.

It did not help Hurley that he had made the announcement without consulting either Wankel or NSU, and in a form which decidedly gave the impression that it was no longer the Wankel engine, but Curtiss-Wright's. In thus changing the name, he was setting a precedent which was followed by other ambitious chief executives anxious to show that it was really *their* rotary engine and not Wankel's. (Even NSU called the engine the NSU-Wankel, but, since they had developed the KKM over Wankel's protests, they were entitled to a share in the credit.)

NSU was furious. They claimed that Hurley had violated the license which, allegedly, provided that neither of the partners should make a separate announcement without permission. Far from backing down, Hurley asked NSU to issue a public statement to the effect that they had given prior permission to him to publicize the engine.

Hutzenlaub took more direct action. He flew to New York, booked a conference room in the Waldorf-Astoria Hotel, and told Hurley that if he did not publicly admit that the Wankel engine was a German invention, he would personally give a press conference and show him up. Hurley, apparently, checked to see if the room had indeed been booked, found that Hutzenlaub was telling the truth, and came out with a supplementary, explanatory statement.

Hurley's troubles with the SEC and NSU did nothing to abash his enthusiasm. In December 1959 he announced a joint venture into solar energy, and in February 1960 he revealed a new type of swiveling propeller made of glass fiber which would, apparently, enable airplanes to take off vertically and then fly horizontally. But in the short term the news was less bright. The results for 1959, announced at the same time as the magic propeller, showed sales down by a fifth (though at $329 million they were higher than a decade later), and earnings had dropped by over forty percent to $1.71 a share. Unabashed, Hurley compiled in the annual report a month later more details of a venture which combined the new propeller and the rotary engine—a six-passenger plane, capable of a speed of 400 miles per hour, with a range of 900 miles, having small wings and four "rotating combustion" engines.

Not surprisingly, trouble was mounting for Hurley. At the company's annual general meeting, there were over three hours of criticisms: by John and Lewis Gilbert, two brothers well known for their attendance at the meetings of troubled companies, and by one Abraham Uchitelli of Great Neck, who "made a dozen speeches complaining that his letters had not been answered and that he had not been able to gain admission to some Curtiss-Wright plants." Hurley fought back, rebutted criticisms of the rotary "by our rivals" and said that a new ignition system had cured the overheating problem. What was more, Curtiss-Wright was developing a new model of hovercraft, and again mentioned the "swing propellor" plane as suitable for interurban travel. Again, Hurley's concept, involving vertical takeoff and landing (VTOL) and quiet rotary engines, was remarkably suitable for the pollution-conscious 1970s.

A month later, the board had had enough. Hurley resigned "to devote more attention to new products" after eleven years as chief executive. After him there was to be no more of his one-man rule. An executive committee of three "independent businessmen" was appointed to run the company, and T. Roland Berner, a Harvard-educated lawyer who had been on the Curtiss-Wright board since 1949, was made chairman. Retrenchment was the order of the day. Within a few months, the company had given away its prototype nuclear reactor to Penn State University, had sold a foam plastics division, and had sold—to General Motors—the research facilities Hurley had built up in California.

Inevitably, Hurley's ambitious plans for the rotary engine also suffered. At first Curtiss-Wright's new bosses suspected that there was some sort of Swabian plot involving Bentele and NSU to make suckers out of the Americans. Although this suspicion was dispelled after a visit to NSU by a Curtiss-Wright director, there would not, said Berner, be any question of producing any engine for the market in the foreseeable future, until there had been "considerably more development on the engine." As an indication that things really had changed from the publicity-happy days of Hurley, he firmly declared that "until products had been fully developed and proved sound, they would not be publicized . . . we will emphasize quality rather than quantity." In the short term, this was fair enough. Some well-qualified observers within Curtiss-Wright had felt that Hurley's approach to the engine was the wrong one, that it took longer to fiddle with individual faults in a new engine than to complete the full analysis which Bentele and Jones had started. But inevitably, the more ambitious projects were abandoned, and even now, fourteen years later, Curtiss-Wright has still not gone into production with any form, shape, or size of rotary engine.

8

A Profitable Tomorrow

"Tomorrow is here. It arrived on November 23rd, 1959."
—KARL LUDVIGSEN, *Sports Cars Illustrated*

Before Hurley had trumpeted the news of "his" engine across the world's front pages, its existence had been known only to a handful of auto industry executives. In the fifteen years since Hurley's announcement, it has firmly, if intermittently, been in the public's consciousness—such was the true measure of Hurley's contribution to the rotary cause.

The immediate reaction to the news—from the press if not from Hurley's colleagues or the SEC—was overwhelmingly favorable, if also, like Hurley himself, wildly optimistic.

By far the best account in the United States was by Karl Ludvigsen in *Sports Cars Illustrated* in February 1960. It was technically so clear that a father-and-son team of do-it-yourself enthusiasts in Florida built themselves a working model of a Wankel engine within a few weeks purely on the information he provided.

Other accounts were less scrupulously descriptive. "It's not for sale yet," reported *Time* magazine, "but NSU expects to have it debugged and in large-scale production in about two years." "There's no question that there will be a revolution coming," declared the leading German motoring magazine, *Auto, Motor und Sport*, which provided the first full account of the engine in Germany together with a report of a mysterious test vehicle with a rotary engine installed in an NSU Prinz car body.

Even the usually caustic magazine *Der Spiegel* was impressed. "It is certain," it reported, "that the NSU-Wankel engine will have a lasting effect on the technology of machine construction and the production of energy." After the *Auto, Motor und Sport* article, NSU claimed it was being forced to spell out details of the engine. This was the first demonstration of the successful balancing technique of NSU's press office, run by Edward Westrop, which contrived to keep public interest in the engine going right through the 1960s, while not running to Hurleyesque flights of the imagination. Even before the announcement, NSU said it had been receiving letters from potential Prinz customers wondering whether they should wait until the new engine was available—the very last situation NSU wanted. Walter Froede said firmly that "on no account will there be an NSU car with a Wankel engine available in 1960." To which von Heydekampf added, "Most probably not in 1961 either."

Hurley's announcement had obviously helped NSU by publicizing the engine, but a much more solid boost was provided by a meeting of the German engineers' professional institution, the Verein Deutscher Ingenieure (VDI), in Munich in February 1960. This had been called, not because of the work of Wankel himself, who was widely thought of as an unsound engineer, but because of the enthusiastic backing of Walter Bensinger, the head of engine development at Daimler-Benz, who had been one of Wankel's assistants on the development of rotary-valve engines during the war. The meeting was held at the Deutsches Museum in Munich, and nearly 3,000 engineers turned up to hear the engine explained by Froede and by some leading professors of engineering. (Bentele, the only Wankel expert missing, had been prevented from attending by Hurley, who was afraid he might give away some of Curtiss-Wright's secrets.)

The VDI meeting made the engine respectable. It also ensured that Daimler-Benz would finally become involved. Professor Friedrich Nallinger, Bensinger's superior as the director in charge of engineering (a job all the more important because the company was heavily engineering-oriented in those days), made a verbal promise to the NSU executives that his company would carry out its own tests on rotary engines of its own design and would behave just like an ordinary licensee. There would be no immediate formal contract, but one would follow later.

All this activity had not been unnoticed by the stock market. When the Curtiss-Wright contract was signed in 1958, the NSU shares had bounced up to DM 550 (550 Deutsche marks), four times the level they had been the year before.

But there was no further news of the rotary in the year following the sale of the Curtiss-Wright license, and NSU's first venture into auto production—a gamble on which the company's future clearly rested—was going badly. The rear-engined NSU Prinz, introduced in 1958, was mechanically promising, but its puddinglike, rounded body work deterred potential buyers. The shares slipped back to 300 and languished around that figure.

The Dresdner Bank, which still had controlling interest in NSU, was so unhappy that it encouraged two deals, either of which would have spelled the end of NSU's independence. The first was a straight takeover by Volkswagen (VW). The second was that Hurley buy half the company's shares, after which Curtiss-Wright and the bank would run it as a joint venture.

Von Heydekampf successfully persuaded the Dresdner Bank not to back either deal, realizing that life under Hurley would have been far worse than control by the Dresdner Bank, and that, had VW gained control, its notoriously anti-Wankel boss, Professor Nordhoff, would have abandoned the rotary and transformed NSU itself into merely another component factory for VW.

But as soon as the engine had been explained to the press in the middle of January 1960, the NSU shares started to zoom up again on the rather narrow German stock markets. The Dresdner Bank took full advantage of the boom, and of an issue, in February 1960, of new shares to existing shareholders in NSU (a "rights" issue). This was carried out in the euphoric atmosphere created by Hurley's announcement and the VDI meeting. By not taking up its allocation, the bank effectively reduced its stake considerably. But the bank did more. Richter and Vierhub had been under severe attack within the bank for years because of NSU's problems, and the money poured out on the engine. Auto industry executives had made plain to other Dresdner Bank directors how ridiculous they thought the idea of the Wankel.

So this was a heaven-sent opportunity for Richter and Vierhub to show what a winner they had nursed all the time. In the early months of 1960, the bank sold half its shareholding at prices which ranged between DM 1,000 and DM 3,000, making a profit of at least $20 million. In one fell swoop they justified all the care and attention the bank had lavished on the company since it was first landed with the shares thirty years before. The bank defended these sales by saying they had been carried out "to combat the madness in the development of NSU shares." Once the bank had unloaded and reduced its holding to below the blocking figure of twenty-five percent, the market, starved of shares, soared even further, reaching a peak in June of around DM 3,200, ten times the price the previous year. Much of the stock was bought by companies controlled by Max Bunford, the industrial banker, who ended up controlling over a quarter of the equity but found himself locked into his holding.

"I became a prisoner; I could not sell without creating a panic," he complained.

After the stock-market hysteria of the preceding six months, NSU's annual general meeting in late July was a long and stormy affair with about 350 shareholders present (usually there were perhaps thirty-five shareholders at a meeting which would last only a quarter of an hour). The small shareholders had banded themselves together under a local Stuttgart doctor, Dietrich Albers. They were highly suspicious of the bank's tactics and were annoyed that they had not, they felt, had a fair allocation of the proceeds of the rights issue. Richter and Heydekampf tried to calm the meeting, but not excite the share price even more, by pointing out that Curtiss-Wright would be producing 100-hp engines that year, but that NSU's hopes of a proper financial return on the $8 million spent so far on Wankel development were strictly long term. This performance quieted the market, but not for long.

The next month a small shareholder wrote innocently to NSU asking about the company's plans for production of vehicles containing the engine. At the end of the month, he received a reply from one of von Heydekampf's assistants, Dr. Hirsch, stating that serious production of a 400-cc engine producing 45 to 55 bhp at a mere 5,000 rpm would start the next year and that it would be installed not only in a Prinz-sized car but in a boat as well. The shareholder naturally showed the letter to friends; the market promptly rose by 200. NSU denied that the letter meant anything; Hirsch was invited to leave the company's service; and the excitement subsided.

By the autumn, von Heydekampf had forbidden journalists to visit NSU to stop any further rumors, but the shares continued to bob about (the Dresdner Bank was accused of alternately encouraging its clients to buy the shares and then trying to damp down the price by refusing to accept the shares as security for loans). The next bout of speculation occurred at the end of the year when NSU showed its dealers a Prinz-sized car with a Wankel engine in it—the model foreseen in Hirsch's letter. The dealers were naturally impressed, and the shares promptly rose another 100.

Early in December Richter and von Heydekampf again tried to damp down the shares by sending out a gloomy interim report on the company's performance in 1960 and prospects for 1961. Motorcycle sales were only half of the level they had reached in 1955; domestic sales in the small car market were down; exports had fallen because of a credit squeeze in Britain. The scooter market, once NSU's mainstay, also "is less lively."

As for the NSU Wankel engine, Richter emphasized just how long-term the prospects were:

We must reiterate what was said at the July 1960 AGM [annual general meeting]. Tests on the bench and in vehicles are continuing and have confirmed our basic technical theories. Our repeated comments on the financial effects, which will only bear fruit in a few years' time at the earliest, are, however, not taken seriously enough in many quarters.

What is more, the new, cautious Berner regime at Curtiss-Wright was having an effect on development overseas.

No further license agreements had been signed, which meant that "larger revenues cannot be expected before full-scale production with long preparation periods."

The report had the desired effect, and the shares dropped by 600 to 1,200 in a mere eight days. But then a suspicion arose that the Dresdner Bank was pushing the share price down to acquire more shares. According to Der Spiegel, Wankel, "with all the fool's license of the inventor," entered the fray, accusing the Dresdner Bank of "trying the same bluff again."

The Dresdner Bank promptly threatened to sue him, but was persuaded not to by William Keppler, who had worked closely with the bank before and during the war when settling Germans on land confiscated in occupied countries. This was the last of the many services rendered to Wankel by Keppler, who died later that year.

Publicly the bank was accused by Dr. Engler, a Düsseldorf

lawyer who represented a few shareholders, of "making the shares go down after selling its own." Dr. Albers formed a permanent club of small shareholders to help protect themselves, advising them all not to sell.

There was a final round of speculation when the irrepressible Albers found out that Daimler-Benz was testing a Wankel engine. Wanting to flush the company out into the open, he spread the rumor that Daimler-Benz had already paid $5 million for a license fee. The rumors finally were quashed, though not before another stormy annual general meeting in 1961 where von Heydekampf explained, "The pregnancy of the NSU Wankel engine, which is bound to take its time, has not yet quite finished."

By that point, however, NSU's orthodox business had recovered sufficiently to carry it over the next few troubled years of Wankel development.

A key factor in NSU turnabout was its redesigned Prinz. It had commissioned the Italian stylist, Michelotti, to redesign the body of the rear-engined vehicle, giving it a distinct resemblance to the crisp, square lines of the much larger Chevrolet Corvair, which came out at much the same time. The Prinz had always handled well and was, mechanically, an adventurously and soundly designed car. This restyled version, launched at the end of 1960, made it a popular choice in a number of European markets (for example, it became the only German automobile to sell well in Italy where small, fast, economical cars with good handling qualities were greatly appreciated).

But NSU could not live by the Prinz alone. It also had to try to make some money from the Wankel. The most obvious way for NSU to make some profit and spread the engine's development costs was to sell more licenses. At first NSU was more interested in showing off the engine than in keeping its innovations secret. It soon learned a sharp lesson when Renault, the French auto company, was allowed to run an engine for 100 hours. Their engineers stated that their company had already developed a rotary engine and that their interest in the Wankel was purely academic. But they studied the Wankel's sealing system with particular care, and a few days after they had returned to Paris, Renault tried to take out patents on a sealing system with a suspicious resemblance to the Wankel's grid. NSU intervened, and Renault explained that they were interested in developing a sealing system for the Cooley rotary engine they were then (unsuccessfully) developing with American Motors.

Wankel was very upset at the loose security around the engine and accused NSU of "incomprehensible gullibility" in allowing such freedom of access. Von Heydekampf, however, was not too worried about the possible infringement of the Wankel patents.

"Our greatest competition," he said, "is still the perfected mass-produced conventional piston engine." On the other hand, the idea, originally Wankel's, and then taken over by NSU, of a "Wankel Club," with development undertaken by a group of companies which would pool the patents and know-how, was being applied only patchily.

NSU had an excellent agent in Japan, the half-Japanese Walter Jensen, and in 1961 two Japanese companies, the medium-sized Toyo Kogyo and the much smaller Yanmar Diesel had both taken out licenses for the manufacture of Wankel engines. In 1960 Fichtel and Sachs, the German manufacturers of industrial engines, secured a license as did four German manufacturers of diesel engines in the following year to form a sort of subsidiary "Diesel Club." These deals brought in a welcome flow of cash—up to $5 million in the case of Toyo Kogyo—but created the most glaring legal loopholes.

Daimler-Benz did not take a formal license for eighteen months after Professor Nallinger had casually agreed to one after the VDI meeting in February 1960. Originally, Hutzenlaub had hoped "to celebrate the signing at the Oktoberfest"—the 1960 autumn beer festival in Munich. The new chairman of Daimler-Benz, Dr. Hitzinger, was most reluctant to go ahead with a license, but Nallinger refused to renege on his verbal promise. Nevertheless, Hitzinger succeeded in reducing the sums his company had to pay considerably, even though his engineers had been learning NSU's secrets ever since the Munich meeting. Finally Daimler-Benz signed an agreement in October 1961, committing itself to an entrance fee of $750,000, payable in three installments.

This contract created a conflict with Curtiss-Wright. Daimler-Benz naturally wanted the right to sell in the United States any rotary-engined vehicles it made. There were two obstacles in their way: Under the 1958 agreement Curtiss-Wright had the right to object to any other company's selling rotary-engined vehicles in the

United States and showed no sign of giving permission; NSU's distributors in the United States, Trans-Continental Motors, run by another German émigré, Fred Oppenheimer, had also been granted the right to veto the import of Wankel-engined vehicles not constructed by NSU, as well as a royalty on the sale in the United States of automotive rotary products. Oppenheimer was valuable to NSU because in the first years of the Prinz, when sales in Europe were sticky, he took several thousand off NSU's hands, and sold them during the first imported-car boom in the United States. At this point, Oppenheimer waived his rights—subject to some form of compensation to be agreed in the future, a condition which has led so far to twelve years of lawsuits. He settled his company's claim against NSU only in 1970—eight years later—and has still not agreed to terms on his personal claim with Wankel and Hutzenlaub.

Renegotiating the contract with Curtiss-Wright took several years—and a lawsuit. In 1961 NSU claimed $20 million on a variety of grounds, including alleged restraint of trade and violations of the antitrust acts. Eventually, three years later, NSU, Wankel, and Curtiss-Wright devised a new agreement, by which all three parties had to give permission for any new type of car with a rotary engine to be imported into the United States—in return for which Curtiss-Wright promised not to block access to the U.S. market. Curtiss-Wright got ten percent of the license fees paid on engines made and sold outside the United States (though it got nothing from royalties on individual engines) and seventy-five percent on rotary cars imported into the United States, so that Curtiss-Wright takes around $10 for every Mazda car exported by Toyo Kogyo to the United States. It also takes sixty percent of sublicense fees and royalties. The remainder was divided sixty–forty between NSU and Wankel's private company of which, by then, Hutzenlaub owned half.

The renegotiation with Curtiss-Wright also exposed another weakness in the old arrangement. For it was clear by then that the company would not be producing its own rotary-engined vehicles of any sort. Bentele and Jones had continued their fundamental analyses under a shifting succession of chief engineers, some more sympathetic than others to the idea of the rotary engine. Jones continues his work at Curtiss-Wright, but within a couple of years of Hurley's departure, Bentele had been eased out of a real job into a consultancy role not directly connected with the development of the rotary. He left the company altogether in 1967.

Curtiss-Wright has never shown much appreciation for the very fundamental contribution Bentele made to the rotary engine. In 1972, when he decided to give his papers on the development of the engine to the Automotive Section of the Detroit Public Library, Curtiss-Wright even tried to stop him on the grounds that the papers had been accumulated while he was a Curtiss-Wright employee, and the papers belonged to the company.

Curtiss-Wright had been less of a drag on the engine's progress in the United States since William Figart was appointed manager of their Rotary Division the year Bentele left, but though Figart has been able to marshal technical evidence when selling to other potential licensees, like General Motors, he has not been able to expend much capital on the project.

The coupon-clipping, unadventurous attitude of Curtiss-Wright's board (largely composed of patent experts and lawyers like the chairman) has denied the engine the promotion it needed in the United States. But this attitude has proved extremely valuable to the company's financial solvency. Curtiss-Wright to this day is the only public company to have actually benefited financially from the Wankel. If it is now a much smaller company than it was in Hurley's day and has had a checkered profit record since 1958, the purchase by General Motors of a Wankel license in 1970 has meant a major windfall for the company, which got five-elevenths of the income involved. As a result, in 1972, the Wankel provided Curtiss-Wright with over $2 million—the alleged cost of that year's rotary research. Since the company has long written off against previous profits on the engine, the $32 million it has supposedly spent on rotary research since 1958, the profit is respectable and accounted for around half the earnings available to Curtiss-Wright's shareholders that year.

Curtiss-Wright was not the only licensee with whom NSU had problems in the early 1960s. In June 1963, Toyo Kogyo announced that it would be exhibiting a rotary-engined car at the Frankfurt Motor Show that September. NSU had its own plans to show the first rotary-engined car, its Spyder, and was determined not to be upstaged by the Japanese. Dr. Paschke, the NSU engineer who had been largely responsible for developing the KKM, was dispatched to

Japan and came back highly impressed. The Japanese threat was clearly no idle one. So NSU warned the Japanese that the license they had bought entitled them only to sell the engine in Asia. According to Jensen, the NSU agent in Japan, this "had the effect of a cold shower" on Toyo Kogyo. That company then climbed down, saying that the whole affair had been an unhappy misunderstanding and that the show referred to was not at Frankfurt, but the tenth All-Japan Motor Show.

The affair provoked Felix Wankel himself into one of his attacks on NSU. "I could imagine nothing more positive than a combined show of all models under license up till now, so that all the progress on the engine can be clearly visible." He thoroughly sympathized with the Japanese, who, he said, "go about it with more élan" than NSU. (He has also been heard to express admiration for Japan as "the land of the kamikaze.") But this irritation was also expressed in more general terms. Wankel returned to the attack on the subject of NSU's carelessness over letting competitors see the rotary—the attitude that had led to the problems three years before with Renault. "One can't," he declared, "send off all one's know-how in installments without knowing what will happen to it."

His advice had, in fact, already been taken. In 1962, NSU had, for the first time, taken on a full-time head for their Legal Department, Dr. Gunther Henn. (Tetzner, the lawyer who had foreseen correctly that Wankel would not show much further interest in the engine, was an outside consultant.) He had worked in the Legal Department of the European Investment Bank during the first four years of the European Common Market. Henn, a stocky, tough, and able lawyer, with a rough and hectoring manner, had ambitions to be recognized as a major authority on international licensing agreements, a desire which coincided exactly with NSU's need to get some order—and more profit—out of the license and patent situation. In the year after his arrival (apart from renegotiating with Toyo Kogyo and Curtiss-Wright), Henn concentrated on producing a standard agreement. When he arrived, licensees used to sign a short three- or four-page document covering only the most basic patents. Henn produced a much more elaborate affair, with seventy clauses, over fifty of which were standard, and he refused to let any more licenses be signed until he had finished working out what they should contain. This was one reason why no new licensees were signed up in 1962 or 1963.

Henn divided up the patents so that every licensee was sure of what he was actually buying. There were three classes. The first contained the three basic patents covering the shape and sealing of the engine. These are completely in NSU's hands and provide the basic coverage up to 1978 in Europe and, because of the four-year delay in getting the license, up to 1982 in the United States. The second group of eighty-eight patents are those considered "economically important." They cover such crucial items as the "window," the tiny channel in the rotor housing that leads from the spark plug to the rotor chamber and allows the spark to get at the combustible mixture, which was taken out by Curtiss-Wright. The spread of these patents shows clearly the value of the Wankel Club to other licensees—and to NSU. NSU had filed fifty-seven of the eighty-eight, Toyo Kogyo eight, Daimler-Benz and Curtiss-Wright seven each, Nissan—a relative newcomer to the club—five, and Fichtel and Sachs two. These patents do not run out until the late 1980s; they represent an immense amount of development work, much of it not done by NSU. Many of them should provide further profit for NSU and a privileged position for the license holders, even after the basic patents have expired.

Then there is an immense group of over 800 patents of lesser importance (300 of which were taken out by Toyo Kogyo, and over 150 by Daimler-Benz, indicating the quantity of detailed research these two companies have done on the engine). But the dividing line between the second and third group is pretty fluid. With the present emphasis on fuel economy, some of Curtiss-Wright's patents, like those covering stratified-charge rotary engines (see page 223), are likely to be transferred to class two.

Henn's standard agreement provides the licensees with a menu of possibilities, and the fees payable depend not just on the size of the company involved, but on the scope of the patent coverage as well. Licensees have, obviously, to take a license for the top three patents, but need not pay for the other groups. General Motors, which has a very exceptional agreement, wanted only the most basic coverage, in its case, covering seven patents only.

New licensees can also choose whether they want merely a bilateral arrangement by which other licensees will not benefit from patents they take out in the course of development or whether they will become a full member of the club and share in the worldwide pool. (The customer also has to decide how much help it wants from NSU.)

Henn had no intention of allowing companies to take out broad licenses like that of Curtiss-Wright. Far more engines could be sold if each licensee was limited in the size of engine involved, the uses to which it could be put, and where it could be sold. Outboard Marine, for example, had to take out two separate licenses: one with NSU covering marine applications throughout the world and a much narrower one with Curtiss-Wright covering a different range of applications within the United States. The range varies from General Motors, allowed to make engines for any possible use except aircraft and not obliged to tell NSU of any of its developments, to Johannes Graupner, whose 1967 license covers only tiny engines ranging from one-tenth to three horsepower for power models and toys.

A distinction was also made between the sale of an engine in a vehicle and one sold loose to an outside customer. This has caused a number of disagreements, including a notable one with Toyo Kogyo, and was one of the areas renegotiated with Curtiss-Wright in the early 1960s.

Henn then defined the minimum level of payment—partly to provide some inducement for the licensee to produce the engine in quantity as soon as practicable; for instance, both Ford and American Motors had clauses in their licenses that provided for a maximum total payment however many engines they produced, and General Motors' original agreement ensures that it will pay no royalties at all on any engines it may make. Henn's new license also had the standard clause, foreshadowed as early as 1958 in the first agreement with Curtiss-Wright, providing for a minimum level of royalty fees after a certain date (in Curtiss-Wright's case it was 1964) even if the company had not put the engine into production. In this way, Henn hoped, all the licensees would take their obligations to produce seriously.

When dealing with large international groups, NSU had to make sure that the actual company acquiring the license could not automatically spread the patents and know-how to the hundreds of companies with which the licensee was associated. For instance, when GKN, the large British auto component company, was seeking a license, it first applied through one of its smaller subsidiaries. But Henn insisted that the parent group take out the license. Similarly, when Fordwerke, Ford's German subsidiary, took out a license, a specific clause had to be written in giving it the right to transmit information back to the parent company.

Each license is still individually tailored and its final form a matter of some rough calculations followed by some tough bargaining. A typical case is Toyota, the biggest Japanese auto maker, which signed, in May 1971, a lease originally covering only petrol-engined cars from 75 to 150 bhp. The usual option to renegotiate the license was exercised in 1973 when Toyota acquired the additional rights to install rotary engines in "other land vehicles," in this case its jeep model, the Toyota Landcruiser.

Toyota's minimum royalty payments start in the fourth year at about $800,000 (the same as Nissan's, but only a third of the figure Toyo Kogyo is currently paying), and by the seventh year Toyota will be on the top rate, in this case $2 million. The arithmetic behind this figure is fairly crude: Henn assumed that forty percent of Toyota's annual production of 2 million vehicles is covered by the range of horsepower in the license, and that one quarter of that forty percent would have rotary engines within seven years. He assumed that each engine would cost about $600 and that the appropriate royalty would be five percent of the value. This gives a theoretical figure of $6 million. Then the bargaining started, and in the end Toyota agreed to pay just $2 million, though Henn claims that he did not ask for the whole of the $6 million. In addition, the five-percent figure was higher than the three percent usually given as a standard fee, though Nissan and Toyota will both be paying it on any engines they produce.

Thanks largely to Henn's efforts, NSU now receives more income from patent fees and royalties than any other single firm in Germany, nearly a tenth of all the income received in Germany from abroad from patents and know-how. His work and the growing strength of NSU's bargaining position as more companies joined the club have also ensured that other companies could not repeat Daimler-Benz's success in getting a wide license for virtually nothing. Where Daimler-Benz had paid under $1 million entrance fee over a period of years, in 1973 the much smaller American Motors had to pay $0.5 million simply as an initial down payment for the patent rights, exclusive of any royalties payable on engines they might build.

Henn and Hutzenlaub actually negotiated most of the licenses. But they could not cover the whole world and therefore left some potential customers unattended. The Russians have often expressed great interest in the engine. (NSU actually sold a license for $1 million to the East Germans in 1965, arousing great criticism in the right-wing press until it became clear that the Communists would have built an engine anyway with or without a license.) For some years, neither Henn nor Hutzenlaub had the time to visit Russia, though they sent a couple of ambassadors in the shape of two NSU RO80 cars. But in 1974, the Russians sent a team of high-powered technicians to Neckarsulm and are clearly now seriously interested in taking out a license—rather later than they might have done if NSU had had a more organized network of agents. Similarly, the Indians have expressed an interest, but without an active network of agents (similar to the very successful Walter Jensen in Japan who was on the scene well before Henn's arrival), sales are bound to be patchy.

Right through the engine's history, there have been skeptics who refused to believe that the engine's patent coverage was as thorough as NSU made out, though their sniping has died down considerably since 1970, when General Motors, able to afford all the legal advice in the world, took out a license. Before that NSU, a small company, was vulnerable to threats. One of the immensely rich Quandt brothers who controlled BMW (Bayerischen Motoren Werke) once telephoned Hutzenlaub in the middle of the night and told him to provide their company with a license agreement free of charge; otherwise the BMW engineers would destroy the NSU patents in court. Hutzenlaub told him to go ahead and try, which BMW apparently did, with no success for over two years.

So, thanks to the strength of the patent net around the engine, the Wankel Club dreamed of by Wankel, Hutzenlaub, and Henn had the chance to flourish. But it only really worked when its members were a small band of enthusiasts, mostly from medium-sized companies, beleaguered by the skepticism of the bigger companies. There were a couple of gatherings of the club, the first in 1965, where information was freely exchanged. But then, as the engines neared or entered production, cooperation dwindled, and Toyo Kogyo in particular has been attacked by the other licensees for not providing the information it should under its agreement. For as time goes on, the amount of sheer technical and production know-how involved grows steadily more important in relation to the patents themselves.

9

The First
Rotary Cars

"The sixth motor in your RO80 should not influence you
decisively in favor of the piston engine. Please go right ahead and
buy the seventh engine; otherwise wait for the gas turbine."
—Horoscope for motorists in German calendar for 1974

NSU could not live from license fees alone. Even to make the
Wankel Club a reliable long-term proposition, NSU had to be a
center for all aspects of rotary technology. Its meager resources
were, therefore, doubly stretched; it had to continue to work on all
types of rotary engines—air-cooled as well as water-cooled, large and
small, for aircraft or chain saws or any other purpose a licensee might
require. If its share of the rotary patents ever fell below a half of the
total, then the life of the club would be limited until the end of the
1970s when the protection provided by the three key patents disap-
peared. At the same time, NSU had to quickly show the world and its
shareholders the potential of the rotary engine in a car.

NSU was clearly not going to get much help from the inventor.
Once the KKM—and not his own preferred DKM—had emerged as
the rotary engine of the future, Wankel's own role in development
was minimal, apart from work carried out under contract for Bensinger, his former assistant. Only once did NSU manage to get him to
help with their sealing problems, even though his contract obliged
him to bear forty percent of the research burden. His typical reaction
to their problems was to read to the NSU executives extracts from

87

the life of Rudolf Diesel. These proved, according to Wankel, that it had taken Diesel thirty years to perfect his type of engine. By implication, it would be just as long before the rotary became a practical proposition.*

The shape of many of the components of a practical rotary engine had, by the early 1960s, already been established by the work done by Froede and Paschke, and by Bentele and Jones at Curtiss-Wright. The dream of a very light aluminum rotor soon faded. Cast iron was essential; even though heavier, it alone could provide the necessary strength. From the beginning, the rotor, like the moving parts of a reciprocating engine, was cooled by oil circulating within it. But it took some 3 million miles of testing before Froede was finally prepared to accept that the oil cooling the rotor was never used up, but simply recirculated endlessly. Even with a part of the motor like this, relatively uncontroversial in theory, it took years to design the shape for the interior of the rotor to ensure that the oil was circulated thoroughly by the rotor's own movement, without acting as a brake on the circular motion.

The two major problems that Froede and Paschke faced when designing the world's first production rotary engine for cars were the apex seals and where to put the ports to allow the engine to breathe. In a rotary, as we have already seen, the engine breathes in air and fuel and, after the completion of the compression and firing stages of the cycle, exhales the burnt gases through ports (holes) either in the side housing or in the curved rotor housing. In either case, the control of the breathing exhaust is achieved not by a complicated system of valves, as in a reciprocating internal combustion engine, but by the movement of the rotor itself. Peripheral ports clearly enjoy a major advantage: The chamber can breathe in fully the whole time one face of the rotor is passing it by, until it is cut off sharply by the apex seal and a new rotor face emerges to be fed. By contrast, if the ports are in the side housing, they are opened and closed more gradually by the flat side of the rotor as it lurches around. The peripheral port, therefore, gives a better opportunity for the engine to breathe more deeply and to exhale more completely than with the side ports, inevitably blocked by the approaching face of the side of the rotor. So a peripheral port will be chosen for any

* This idea was vehemently refuted by Diesel's son, who wrote to the press saying that his father had taken fifteen, not thirty, years to perfect his engine.

engine designed to be run at high speeds with high efficiency, since the power output can be increased quite simply by pushing through more combustible mixture by opening the inlet ports more widely. (There is the additional advantage that with a side port the tube containing the air-fuel mixture has to be turned through a right angle around the engine before it can be fed into the rotor chamber, whereas with peripheral ports it can go straight in.)

Inevitably, there is a price to be paid for the efficiency of the peripheral port, as NSU was to discover through painful experience during the 1960s. To provide the best conditions for efficient breathing, the inlet and exhaust ports are placed comparatively close together, by the waist of the rotor housing, directly opposite the spark plug; to take Norbye's analogy of a clock face again, if the plug is at three o'clock, the exhaust port will be at eight o'clock and the inlet at ten o'clock. With a peripheral port, this produces "overlap"—mixture is being exhaled and inhaled in and out of the same face at the same time. Engineers were already familiar with this phenomenon; indeed, it is used to improve the power of ordinary reciprocating engines, in which it is known as "valve overlap" because it is the valves and not the ports that are open at the same time.

At low speed, however, a rotary engine with peripheral ports and lots of overlap faces two major problems described as "bucking and snatching" and "three-stroking," noticeable when the engine slows down and when it is idling. After the throttle has been closed because of the peripheral port overlap, the engine continues to take in more fresh mixture than it needs, and there is a time lag before these gases are burned—there is simply too much coming in for the reduced speed of the rotor; so the engine literally "bucks and snatches" like a horse.

"Three-stroking," on the other hand, occurs when an engine is running at low revolutions, allowing a vacuum to develop on the inlet side of the engine. This is partially filled by exhaust gases seeping past the rotor; the seepage spoils the fresh incoming mixture by mixing it with burnt-out gas from the exhaust side and produces a "three-stroking" rhythm—that is, the engine fires three times properly followed by three bad misfirings. This produces a jerkiness of motion entirely unlike the rotary's habitually smooth rhythm.

Licensees tried different solutions to the problem. Toyo Kogyo, of Japan, opted for side inlet ports, accepting their breathing limitations, and reduced the disadvantage by having two side ports, one on each side of the rotor, and by keeping the exhaust ports on the periphery of the housing. The American manufacturer of snowmobiles and outboard motors, Outboard Marine Corporation, developed a double inlet port, a side port used at low speeds and a peripheral port which only opened up when really high-speed power was required. Several licensees experimented with a combi-port, a real compromise, which straddles the corner where the curved housing meets the flat side plate.

NSU and Daimler-Benz insisted on staying with the peripheral port because they wanted the fastest possible car. NSU dodged its problems by eliminating the clutch, as in the company's second rotary-engined car, the RO80. This contained a "fluid convertor coupling" similar to the hydraulic link employed in most automatic transmissions, though the RO80 also had a manual shift. In this way, the bucking and snatching motions are alleviated by the intervention of the transmission and are not transmitted to the wheels. Daimler-Benz replaced the orthodox carburetor with a system of fuel injection, which injects a precisely metered quantity of gasoline into the chamber at the appropriate points in the combustion cycle. Since the fuel pump responds instantly to any movement on the throttle, this reduces problems due to too rich a mixture. It should also eliminate three-stroking because the movement of the rotor makes a flame like a blowtorch in the chamber into which the fuel is injected. And a decade later Suzuki, the Japanese motorcycle manufacturers, produced an engine with no less than three peripheral ports, to try to overcome the problems inherent in this layout.

But all these solutions required time and money, and NSU at least had a limited amount of both commodities. It certainly never had enough of either to solve the engine's central problem, that of sealing the chamber.

The first KKM engine had been only 125 cc in capacity. In July 1959, Froede and Paschke started to test an engine of 350 cc in a first attempt to develop a unit that would power a car. But over the next three years, they waged an unsuccessful battle against the problems of the apex seals. If they used hard materials for the apex seals, the seals scratched the curved internal housing of the rotor. If they used softer materials, the seals leaked badly. Wear on the housing meant replacing the engine component that was most difficult to machine —originally it required over twelve hours of machine time for one housing.

"Leaks" through, around, or under the leading edge of the apex seals meant that some of the fuel-air mixture mixed with the exhaust gases and remained unburnt.

The "chatter marks," regular ripples or wave marks on the housing surface, the product of using a tough iron or steel alloy on the seal tips, haunted all the rotary development teams in turn. These marks were formed when the apex seals were lifted off from the trochoid surface of the housing by the sheer force of the explosion, as well as from friction caused by waste products from combustion and fuel impurities. After the seals had been pushed off the surface of the housing by these bits and pieces, they would thump back down with enough force to splinter or chip the finished surface. At first the chatter marks appeared after only five hours' wear, and as late as the middle of 1962, they were appearing after only 100 hours at cruising speed, around 5,000 to 7,000 rpm. This would allow only 3,000 miles' driving.

NSU was looking for an ideal seal which would be self-lubricating, mechanically strong, of cheap material, and easy to machine yet still tough enough not to be worn down or deformed by the wide range of heat and stresses under which it would be operating. In 1962, they thought they had found the solution. A very hard chrome surface was applied to the inside of the housing, and apex seals were made from a special carbon material developed in conjunction with Morganite the British specialist company in carbon engineering.

By 1962, NSU had also solved another important problem: ignition. Froede and the NSU engineers realized that a special spark plug was required that could stand up to the permanently hot conditions around the combustion zone. The plug and the housing around it were never cooled by a fresh charge of gas and air, as in a reciprocating engine.

In 1962, NSU even marketed a rotary engine to the public for the first time. It was a 300-cc unit called the KKM 150, designed experimentally for use in fire pumps and other small industrial units. But the public could only buy a version adapted for small motorboats used to tow water-skiers. It weighed only twenty pounds, but the starter weighed almost as much.

The success of the engine prompted some buyers to use it as an auxiliary engine for yachts, a use for which it was not suited. Such use strained the engine and gave it a bad reputation. Eventually it was prohibited. For safety reasons, it was laid down that water-skiing "should be done with a boat containing at least three people," which meant that the NSU unit would not be powerful enough.

Finally, the first rotary-engined vehicle ever was sold to the public. NSU's engineers had developed seven different engines before deciding on the one to be installed in a car. It was a single-rotor unit with a displacement of 996 cc (the displacement of a rotary engine is calculated by doubling the volume of the chamber).

The body was inevitably an adaptation of the Prinz; NSU could not afford to experiment with a completely new car. A convertible, or "Spyder" in European terms, the NSU vehicle had a tiny Wankel engine placed in a rear engine compartment that was small anyway, but in which the rotary fitted like a pea in a matchbox.

Rumors about the car started in the summer of 1963, and in September the Spyder appeared at the Frankfurt Motor Show—to great public interest. However, one spectator indifferent to the arrival on the market of the first rotary-engined car was the inventor himself. Wankel refused to be present when production started—a staged event shown on television. He also refused to accept the first Wankel-engined car ever produced on an ordinary assembly line, claiming loftily, "This sort of ballyhoo has never interested me."

The NSU assembly line produced only two or three Spyders a day, and, all in all, only a few thousand were ever sold to the public. Merely to supply every one of NSU's 1,400 dealers in Germany with one rotary car each would have used up a couple of years' production. But the initial demand by the public was enormous, even at the original price of $2,000—a lot for a car in Germany in 1964. Publicity about the car had not been restricted to Germany, but as the news of the car and the engine spread, so did rumors of its unreliability.

The areas where it was said the car gave the most trouble were engine-cooling and ignition. NSU had absolutely no experience of water-cooling. Its motorcycles and the engines of its Prinz cars had all been air-cooled. All licensees had to tell NSU about their research work; so Froede knew the work done by Bentele and Jones on their "stitched-flow" method of cooling the housing by turning it into a honeycomb of passages for the cooling water. But he ignored it and had stuck to cooling only the outside circumference of the engine. In about a fifth of the cars returned to NSU for repair, the ignition was a problem.

But the biggest headache was the sealing. Not only the apex seals, but even the ring of seals placed on the side of the rotor near the central shaft to prevent the oil lubricating the shaft from leaking, were found deficient. The apex seals were the worst. The Spyder had never been adequately tested in the conditions found in everyday driving in cities, the "stop-start" driving in heavy traffic. Under these conditions, the seals quickly became brittle and often fell apart completely. The carbon seals were too stiff anyway; they could not be fabricated into the best possible shape.

All these problems were compounded because there were no mechanics anywhere in the world who could cope with even the smallest repairs on a rotary engine—not even the relatively simple changing of the apex seals. NSU sent token shipments of the car to every possible market as a promotional move, and insisted that "no one who gets a Wankel must be disappointed." The result, in the United States particularly, was a tale of mounting repair costs on a scale that a small company like NSU just could not afford. Fred Oppenheimer, who was still distributing NSU cars at the time, today recalls, "I had a Wankel cemetery in New York for NSU." Apparently NSU insisted that disappointed customers get a completely new engine free. With each of these engines costing $300, plus airfreight, plus taxes, this added up to $600 repair costs for every broken-down Spyder.

But the Spyder was, after all, a pioneer, and the shortcomings it exposed in the engine would not have been fatal to the rotary motor's chances of acceptance if the next rotary-engined model NSU produced had been remotely reliable. It was not. The first car designed to take full advantage of the rotary's advantages was the RO80, a magnificent showpiece for an engine which let it down.

The RO80 appeared to solve all the problems revealed by the Spyder. It had a two-rotor engine to provide the smoothest possible power. Each rotor was equipped with two spark plugs, one in the position on the housing most suitable for cold starting, the other in the best place for hotter conditions. Instead of an ordinary stick-shift, which brought out the problems of low-speed running and deceleration, the RO80 was equipped with a semiautomatic transmission, with no driver-operated clutch. But the design used had a disconcerting trait. If a driver rested his hand on the top of the gear shift, as many drivers do when in heavy traffic requiring frequent gear changes, the clutch automatically disengaged.

In the RO80, the apex seals had been completely redesigned. Instead of having a soft carbon seal running on a very hard housing surface, the RO80 had seals made of cast iron—or rather of IKA, a special piston ring alloy developed during the war by Goetze. These ran on a special silicon surface developed by Daimler-Benz.

The RO80 car looked very handsome. Taking advantage of the engine's compactness, NSU's designers had slung the hood down in front of the front axle. This made an immense amount of room for five people in a medium-sized car. But the car was not, officially, "styled." In the words of the British *Motor:*

To NSU, as to some other engineering-oriented companies, the word "styling" is an anathema; the shape they feel should be a fallout from the proper satisfaction of the car's functions. So it has a very low projecting front fitting tightly over the engine and radiator to give maximum visibility and minimum aerodynamic drag.

The car looked crisp and elegant. In the words of one German consumer questioned by a market research survey: "It seems to be cutting the air even when standing still."

It was aimed to compete for a section of the car-buying market composed of professional men and younger executives in which BMW in particular, and all German car manufacturers in general had enjoyed considerable success. These buyers were more interested in performance and elegance than size or luxury and were prepared to pay handsomely for it.

The RO80 could, therefore, be priced quite high—well over $3,000—justified by its top speed of 100 mph, power steering, semiautomatic transmission, and its handling and acceleration abilities. At the Frankfurt Motor Show in September 1967, it was received with rapture. Two international juries of motoring journalists chose it as "car of the year." Though von Heydekampf had gone out of his way to emphasize that Wankel had had nothing to do with the Spyder's development, even Wankel was happy to accept one. He insisted on a special model with silver-gray paintwork.

When Dr. Richter, NSU's chairman, ordered the same color for his RO80, Wankel described it as "the only time that I ever saw eye to eye with Richter." Another famous customer was Albert Speer, von Heydekampf's old boss, who was presented with the car when he was just out of prison.

Originally NSU produced thirty-five to fifty RO80s a day, less than a tenth of its total volume. But by the end of 1968, production was stepped up and a Saturday shift introduced.

One of the earliest complaints of RO80 owners was about the extremely high gas consumption, just over ten miles per gallon. Another complaint was even more formidable. The new seal-housing combination had never been properly tested at slow speeds or for stop-and-start driving. It was discovered that they suffered from exactly the same problems as the carbon-chrome combination in the Spyder. By the end of 1968, NSU was well aware of the problem. The Development Department was frantically looking for new solutions to the sealing wear problem, while all the time, "they were producing engines that would be back in the workshop tomorrow." According to Jan Norbye, author of the standard technical work on the engine, "The NSU engineers were surprised at the amount of wear found in the engines of cars that had been run a stop-start test cycle."

The car buyers quickly noticed the same thing. A survey was conducted by *Auto, Motor und Sport* of 191 RO80s produced in the last quarter of 1968. The cars had been driven an average of 20,000 miles in the eighteen months between their production and the date of the survey. Twenty-five percent had broken down on the highway at least once; seventy-five percent had had starting trouble; fifty percent had had rotor or bearing failures that required replacement of the entire engine. Overall, 126 had needed a replacement engine for one reason or another. Because NSU had rashly given a guarantee of eighteen months or 25,000 kilometers (just over 14,000 miles), virtually all of these engines had to be replaced free of charge.

The car's troubles, especially with seals, became a joke; when RO80 drivers passed each other, they were supposed to hold up a certain number of fingers to indicate how many sets of seals they had had fitted since they bought the car. The average was supposed to be three.

It took over two years before NSU finally conquered the sealing problem. Keeping IKA for only the side pieces of the seals, NSU engineers found other stronger alloys, like titanium nitride, for the center pieces. But by then the damage to the rotary's public image was enormous; it was condemned as unreliable in the eyes of motorists throughout Europe. Inevitably, within a couple of years production of the RO80 was down to a trickle.

If the story of NSU in the 1960s is that of the doomed pioneer struggling with inadequate time and resources to produce a satisfactory car, that of Daimler-Benz was precisely the opposite. Daimler-Benz developed more than one rotary engine capable of satisfying even its own hypercritical standards of engineering and durability, but an indefinable mixture of financial caution and satisfaction with its orthodox developments has so far inhibited production of any rotary-engined *cars* at all.

There is also an impression that Dr. Friedrich Flick, the rich industrialist who controlled the company until his death in 1974, was against the whole idea. If this were true, it was inevitable that Dr. Zahn, who became chief executive toward the end of the 1960s, was influenced by Flick.

In any case, the 1960s were an unlucky decade for the engine to arrive at Daimler. The company had always been dominated almost exclusively by engineers, who would naturally be anxious to show that they alone could develop a revolutionary new engine to a proper standard.

Other factories' engineers agreed with Daimler's proud self-estimation. For example, Harry Mundy, the chief engine designer for Jaguar, pronounced, "Not until the Mercedes engineers pass the Wankel engine for serious production will it be really respectable in Europe." But during the 1960s Daimler became less engineering dominated and more under the control of financially oriented senior management, a direction that did not bode well for the rotary engine.

Ironically, the Wankel enthusiasts within Daimler started with an immense advantage. The late Dr. Wolf-Dieter Bensinger, the company's chief engine designer at the start of the 1960s, had worked on aircraft engine development as an assistant of Wankel's at Lindau during the war. But unlike Froede at NSU, or Bentele at Curtiss-Wright, Bensinger lacked a boss with the flair, the imagination—or the recklessness—to back the engine wholeheartedly. Bensinger apparently first discussed the engine with Wankel at Lindau in 1960 and started work on testing an NSU unit (which they were surprised worked at all) immediately after NSU had agreed to take a license, and well before the final terms had been agreed upon. He and a small team set to work designing their own engine. At one point in the late 1960s, Daimler was reputed to be spending $1 million a year on the engine, but the average number of engineers engaged on its development was only thirty or so, a tenth of the skilled manpower General Motors was later to employ on rotary developments. In 1961 the first test-bed engine was built. Daimler was primarily interested in bigger vehicles; so even the first test engine had two rotors. The company did make about a dozen one-rotor units and sufficiently developed them to run satisfactorily at the ridiculously low idling speed of 350 rpm for five hours continuously.

Bensinger was in a position where he could get fundamental and applied research done on a satisfactory scale. He commissioned a great deal of work from outside—from Wankel himself and also from university departments of engineering. In his enthusiasm, Bensinger would even issue development and research orders without getting clearance from his superiors. Eventually, Daimler-Benz feared that his enthusiasm was crippling the development of orthodox recip-rocating engines.

The first problems Daimler engineers tackled were peripheral to the engine's most fundamental troubles. The first was too much oil consumption, the result of unsatisfactory sealing. The engines Daimler were testing devoured nearly two pints of oil for every hour of running time and poured out blue exhaust smoke. The cast iron housings were also clearly ineffectual, and Daimler, like other rotary builders, turned to aluminum.

But the lasting contribution made to the engine by Bensinger, his boss Herr Scherenburg, and the present head of Daimler's Rotary Engine Department, Dr. Lamm, was in proving for the first time that the problem of the apex seals could be solved and that an engine could be produced, at least for the luxury market, that could cum-pete with reciprocating units—and weigh much less. Daimler rejected as unsound NSU's having soft carbon seals and a very hard chrome lining to rub against. What they were looking for was two compatible hard substances.

In Lamm's heroic search for the right materials, he first tried ceramics, then quartz. He consulted the leading metallurgical companies in Germany and even tried some powder found in the air extractor vent of a grinding company in Augsburg. Finally, with the help of engineers at Mahle, a major piston manufacturer, Lamm found an alloy of silicon carbide called Elnisil (or Nicasil) described in old patent; it resisted wear and was easily applicable to the rotor housing. He then concentrated on discovering a matching material for the tips of the seals. Here he had a stroke of luck. Fritz Feller, Rolls-Royce's chief engineer, was lunching one day with a friend from Rolls-Royce's central materials laboratories. The friend told him about a new compound they were working on, silicon carbide. This was very hard and could be made very smooth—in technical language, it had a "low coefficient of friction."

This material would work very well for the rotor's seals. But it was expensive—around $20 for enough material for a set of seals for one car. The seal Daimler-Benz made up from the new wonder-ceramic was an immense advance. Not only has it proved extremely durable, but it is very light, a third of the weight of a thicker metallic seal. It has gradually become the standard for rotary engines since the late sixties.

The Daimler-Benz seal's major problem was its cost, which proved too much for NSU executives, who had gone to see Feller while they were frantically looking for better materials for the RO80. NSU was not automatically entitled to the use of the material because their license agreement was only with Rolls-Royce's reciprocating engine division, and therefore did not include the materials laboratory. This asked what seemed to NSU an inordinate price for the material and one which NSU just would not accept—they were thinking in terms of under $1 a seal, while Rolls-Royce's price was far higher. If NSU had paid the asking price, then the RO80's engine would probably not have let down the buyers nearly as badly and this splendid car would have enjoyed the great success it deserved.

Daimler's plans for introducing a rotary-engined car took a knock with the first set of American antipollution regulations in the mid-1960s, a time when the Wankel was still thought of as a dirty engine. But in 1968–69, they came near to producing the rotary dream vehicle for which the motoring world was still waiting.

The dream car was the C-111, developed by Rudi Uhlenhaut, the great engineer who was ending his career as head of development for Daimler. In 1967 Daimler-Benz had just finished a major reorganization of its truck interests, building the biggest truck factory in Europe, and smugly had rather neglected the development of its cars. This standpattism showed up in a surge of sales of BMW cars, often to the younger executives and professional classes—to whom the RO80 was designed to appeal. They had come to feel that owning a Mercedes may have been a sign of maturity and of status, but also of a certain stodginess. Uhlenhaut's avowed intention was to produce a sporty car, which would be the most advanced in the world in every possible way, to recapture the imagination of this disaffected group. It would not be used for racing, for there was no glory to be gained from a Mercedes winning a race, only shame from losing (an attitude shared by Jaguar, formerly Mercedes's great rival), but it would demonstrate that the inventors of the motorcar had not lost their talent for original design.

The C-111 had a rotary engine, first with three rotors, then with four, placed behind the driver. The car itself was largely constructed from fiber glass, with its doors hinged at the top like a gull's wings.

The engine had to be worthy of the car, and by the end of the 1960s it was. The sealing problem had been solved, and so, in a manner typical of Daimler, was the question of combustion. Their engineers demanded perfection, regardless of expense. The solution devised by Scherenburg and Bensinger was fuel injection. The entry of gasoline could be timed so exactly that there would be no question of three-stroking, bucking, snatching, "quiver," or any of the other troubles to which the peripheral-ported rotary was prone. What is more, there would not be one injector per rotor, but two, to make the combustion more accurate.

Daimler even anticipated "stratified-charge" combustion, which came into fashion in the early 1970s (for a full discussion, see page 223). Briefly, stratified charge takes into account the variations in the mixture of gasoline and air needed to get combustion started and to keep it going. If two injectors supply the different areas of the chamber with two different fuel mixtures, depending on how near they are to the spark plug, it will mean cleaner and more complete combustion and maximum efficiency.

Even the three-rotor C-111 seemed to be a salable proposition. A number of millionaires had come with open checkbooks to the motor shows where it was exhibited to try to buy one. What is more, the engine had triumphantly demonstrated the advantages of the rotary. It was so small compared with a 350-bhp orthodox unit that it could be tucked away behind the driver, enabling the C-111 to be a far smaller car overall than it would otherwise have been. And the difference in weight was positively startling. The three-rotor, for instance, producing 350 bhp, weighed only 308 pounds. Ford's V-8 of the same power weighed just twice as much, a weight penalty of three hundredweight (cwt), before taking into account the stronger front suspension needed to carry the extra weight. Daimler's own V-8, introduced at the same time, weighed 200 pounds more than the rotary, yet produced only 230 bhp.

The idea of selling the four-rotor car to the public was almost irresistible. At one point, the Daimler board did agree to produce it in quantity to sell to customers who, it was felt, would not be put off by the very steep price, or the high fuel consumption. In addition, the four-rotor car would be a splendid alternative to the orthodox V-8 being introduced at the same time.

But in the end, a prudent view prevailed. With its enormous power and acceleration—0 to 30 mph in 1.8 seconds, 0 to 100 mph in 14 seconds in the four-rotor version—the car would tempt private motorists to enter it for racing. The car itself was not entirely suitable for regular use by the public. Then there was the simple fear of a new, unproven idea—"there must be no experiments in customers' hands."

This attitude had led the company to delay incorporating even such proved improvements as disk brakes into their cars until long after its rivals. Even today, Daimler manufactures its own design of automatic transmission, whereas even Rolls-Royce accepts a ready-made General Motors unit.

The sales people said that if a four-rotor Mercedes engine or car was to be on sale, the company would have to back it up with two- and three-rotor units to replace its own smaller four- and six-cylinder engines.

Another reason for making two- and three-rotor units was the very large development costs incurred. (Some estimates had placed it at $50 million.) Only by producing rotary units in quantity could components become standardized. But neither the two- nor the three-rotor unit was considered anywhere near ready for the public—not the Mercedes public anyway.

The board was also worried that there had been virtually no research and development on orthodox units. The enthusiasm of Bensinger, Uhlenhaut, and Scherenburg for the C-111 meant that all Daimler's considerable research resources had been devoted to solving the rotary's problems.

The scales were finally tipped against the rotary by the 1973 world fuel crisis, a particularly heavy blow to the national automobile industry where gasoline cost two dollars a gallon *before* 1973. The rotary program was radically slowed down. The official policy was that when a rotary's penalty in fuel consumption went down to five percent, it would be considered. Today the program is not dead, and not entirely in cold storage, but it is certainly not flourishing. Sadly, the company which virtually invented the motorcar has proved too prudent, too aware of financial constraints, to produce a vehicle powered by the first great Swabian engineering invention for seventy years.

10

Bercot and Bunford

NSU clearly did not have the resources to develop the rotary properly; equally obviously, Daimler-Benz was less than wholehearted in its devotion to the Wankel cause. But there was one major European motor company that was a prime candidate for the rotary boosters. The French Citroen company could be expected to welcome an engine which was technically too far out for any other manufacturer to produce.

For Citroen, though controlled by the Michelin family, was run for twenty years after the war by a visionary purist quite unlike anyone else in the auto industry. Pierre Bercot was trained as a lawyer. Slight, with rimless spectacles and thinning hair standing fiercely on end, Bercot gives an appearance of pure, fierce, nonconforming intellectualism. He was, and is, totally scornful of all business theory or motor industry practice. He believes firmly that modern society has evolved too far toward collectivism and indeed developed his anticollectivist views in a number of philosophical works after his retirement in 1970. Naturally, he also believes that business success depends purely on the man at the top. His fierce, uncompromising individualism made him, inevitably, a passionate antitrade unionist, but it did not turn him into a supporter of De Gaulle—against whom he wrote a diatribe (*The Old Age of the Prince*).

The company he ran has had a history of technical boldness. Its founder, the flamboyant André Citroen, had been forced to sell out in 1934 to the Michelins (his biggest suppliers and creditors) just after introducing the deeply beloved *traction avant,* the first front-wheel-drive car produced anywhere in the world in any quantity.

His successors continued the trend. Bercot himself, not surprisingly in view of his strong views on the need for leadership, had no time for the customers' views on the sort of vehicles they imagined they wanted, nor for sales and marketing men who, also, could only see the present situation. For Bercot assumed that his company could anticipate the future, rather than the existing, needs of his customers. Furthermore, the customer was to be provided with the car he really needed, not the one he *thought* he required—one reason why Citroen never advertised its products in France. The policy was pursued with a severe French logic, which ensured that Citroen's cars could not be ignored. Either, like a vast number of French motorists, you became a member of the "Citroen family," and bought a succession of the company's cars or, like the majority of auto drivers, you found them too fantastic to be taken seriously.

The trend started in 1948 with the famous 2 cv *(deux cheveaux)*—designed as a simple box to bump safely and everlastingly over rough French rural roads, and once described by some anonymous motoring buff as "an umbrella over an engine." Later came the slightly bigger Ami 6—also a severely practical small family sedan, whose quite appalling body styling "made it resemble what an ordinary car looks like after an accident." Finally, the space-age DS 19, the sleek luxury model, was introduced in 1955.

All these cars had front-wheel drive. All were designed to stay in production for a generation or more—as they have. For the DS, Citroen designed a hydraulic suspension decades ahead of its time, and inevitably expensive to produce. But Bercot knew that this was what the customers, logically, required. And he finds it ridiculous that other manufacturers have never copied Citroen, merely because its superior suspension costs more to produce than a crude set of leaf springs.

So Bercot was naturally interested in the logic, the simplicity, the challenge of the Wankel, especially as he is still convinced that the idea behind it was first dreamed up by a Frenchman, a certain M. Carnot. Other lesser companies would have sent an engineer to examine the engine. But it was always an inherent part of Bercot's philosophy of management to operate, not through a regular hierarchy, but through individual managers, not necessarily the obvious ones for the task involved. Seniority, or your nominal departmental responsibility, did not mean very much. Typically, his ambassador to

NSU early in 1961 was André Noel, his amiable export director, a soft-spoken former diplomat whose professional skills were much in demand in the succeeding years.

At the time, NSU was negotiating with all the French auto manufacturers except Citroen. So von Heydekampf told Noel that NSU would not let Citroen have an engine unless they took out a license first. At that point, a major new character entered into the foreground of the Wankel story, Max Adolphus Bunford, who, among his other rotary involvements, controlled NSU's interests in France. He was introduced to Bercot by a long-standing mutual friend, Diomède Catroux, the nephew of one of De Gaulle's closest colleagues, and himself a former minister.

The visit was the opening of Bunford's attempts during the 1960s to use the Wankel engine as the pivot around which a truly pan-European auto company could be built. The dream probably never had as much chance of success as Bunford believed. It was a noble idea all the same, though Bunford was a curious apostle for it.

He was born of wealthy, partly Jewish parentage in Austria and educated under the liberal economist Ludwig von Mises at the University of Vienna. (He has always claimed that "he is an economist by vocation but a financier only through necessity.")

He is the complete loner—"I still have a crawling terror of being caught in a community singsong," he declares. He followed his mother to England before the war and had what the British like to describe as "a damned good war." In his case this meant being parachuted more than once behind enemy lines and doing other secret work in the Balkans and the Middle East. He emerged a British citizen.

When he found a substantial parcel of NSU shares in one of his family's bank vaults in Switzerland, he was told by the bank manager they were worthless. But he borrowed a car, drove to see NSU's factory at Neckarsulm, and to his surprise found that it was still standing—with the windows boarded up with cardboard—serving as a repair shop for U.S. Army vehicles. On his next visit to Switzerland, he traded in some of his holding in the German Stahlunion steel company for more NSU stock—a barter transaction because the Swiss bankers were convinced that Germany would never recover from the war and that any German shares were therefore valueless. Bunford soon became a firm supporter and friend of von Heydekampf and contracted to sell NSU's motorcycles in twenty-eight countries (eventually he voluntarily relinquished all his agencies except in France and Britain).°

From the early 1950s, Bunford was convinced that a united Europe was inevitable and desirable. From his first contact with Bercot, they schemed to make it an industrial reality by bringing NSU and Citroen together in some form of joint company involving the rotary engine. "Everything I did at the time was connected with the Wankel," said Bunford.

After three years of argument he succeeded. NSU and Citroen formed a joint company called Comobil, which would combine two unique qualities in one vehicle. In Bunford's words, "NSU would produce the most extraordinary engines to match the extraordinary cars made by Citroen."

The agreement was not easy: Bunford had three barriers to overcome. First, there was the natural French suspicion of any foreign ideas; then, the inevitable resistance by the proudly isolationist and self-sufficient engineers at Citroen; and finally, there were the formidable barriers erected by Citroen's lawyers, who added deep legal misgivings of their own to the generally hostile and superior attitude adopted toward the world by ordinary Citroen employees. Even now, more than a decade later, there is a strong element within Citroen that is still hostile to this intrusion.

Comobil broke down the barriers between the companies, but, otherwise, the joint development was not entirely successful. Within three years it had become clear that NSU could not deliver within the foreseeable future an engine which would fulfill Citroen's requirements for a unit worthy of the small advanced family saloon they were designing to go round it. The Citroen share of the design package later appeared in a slightly enlarged form, and with an orthodox engine, as the Citroen GS family sedan, which was modern enough to show that Citroen, at least, had fulfilled its share of the Comobil bargain. But NSU's progress was slow; every engine they produced was slightly better than its predecessor, showing enough

---

° His friendship and support of von Heydekampf, his influence as a major shareholder of NSU—though one who was never an executive, nor, at his own wish, a director—and his deals in NSU shares have turned him into a highly controversial character, much suspected by some of the other people in the Wankel story. Felix Wankel himself believes that this book is a plot of Bunford's to exaggerate his role in the rotary story and tell it from his viewpoint.

progress for Citroen not to abandon the venture, but not enough to enable any firm production plans to be made. In 1967, Comobil's studies were complemented by a new company called Comotor, the first company formed solely to produce a rotary engine. Both the potential customers for Comotor's products, NSU and Citroen, took forty-eight percent of the equity, as they had with Comobil. Bunford, the honest broker, took the remaining four percent with the option to buy up another three percent from each partner to give him a total potential holding of ten percent.

But before Comobil had been complemented by Comotor, Bunford's ideas had taken an apparently decisive step forward. By 1966-67, Citroen's customers were showing less gratitude than at any time since the war. For the first time since 1945, sales were not rising steadily, inexorably, year by year. There was talk of rationalizing the French motor industry, and it was confidently supposed that Citroen would merge with the proud family firm of Peugeot. But Bercot's arrogance stopped the merger at the last minute; he made it clear to the Peugeot family that their company would merely be a division of the Citroen empire, like Buick or Oldsmobile within General Motors. In June 1966, Peugeot broke off the talks and, instead, announced a link-up with the common rival, the state-owned Renault.

The next month the auto gavotte started. Heinrich Nordhoff of Volkswagen came to talk to Bercot in Paris. His arrival, on a supposedly secret visit, was glaringly dramatic. A helicopter lent by a French company anxious to show their wares to VW whisked him from the airport to a landing stage close to Citroen's Paris headquarters. There he was met by a fleet of the shiny black DS 19s, which provide the standard transport for French ministers.

Bunford's idea was nothing less than a European General Motors: Citroen would merge with NSU; then the enlarged company would itself merge with Volkswagen. The Wankel engine would then have a double shell around it. Its development would be in the hands of a uniquely strong auto company, but it would be protected by Citroen from the direct power of Nordhoff—an avowed skeptic who once described the rotary as a "stillborn child."

It is extremely doubtful if this idea was ever practicable. Bercot enormously admired Nordhoff, the strong man who had built up a major company from nothing by his own efforts. But in 1966–67, it seemed as if Citroen, shorn of a French partner, with nothing to offer the growing minority of motorists who wanted a medium-sized family car, needed help more urgently than VW, and it was never clear that Nordhoff believed totally in the merger. In any event, three other factors frustrated Bunford's dream. One was German nationalism; another was Nordhoff's illness and death in 1967; and the third was the Israeli-British Bank (IBB).

The IBB was an investment bank, operating in Israel and Britain, with strong links to a number of Swiss banks, links that led to an outflow of funds, which, in 1974, proved big enough to bankrupt it. Its former managing director, Joshua Bension, was, indeed, convicted of fraud as a result of the collapse. But all this was in the future when, in 1966, one of their investment advisors, William Gutfreund, became a Wankel enthusiast. By that time rumors had already begun to circulate about the RO80; the Prinz was selling well; and a large number of licensees had paid their entrance fees to the Wankel Club, and many were rumored to be on the verge of producing engines or vehicles. The IBB, like many other Jewish financial institutions, had never previously invested in postwar Germany and was still reluctant to do so, but after much heart-searching the directors yielded to Gutfreund's enthusiasm. The bank started to buy NSU shares through Swiss nominee accounts and within a few months had built up a seven-percent holding in shares. This made the bank the third largest shareholder in NSU. The largest was still the Dresdner Bank, although its holding was under twenty-five percent. The second was Max Bunford, who at one point owned or effectively controlled over a quarter of the equity, but who in the mid-1960s was, on balance, a seller of the shares. The situation was further confused because, in addition to the shares it actually owned, the Dresdner Bank also controlled the votes of shares owned by investment clients. Probably Bunford and the bank between them controlled nearly half NSU's capital.

The IBB's camouflaged buying campaign surprised the stock market. NSU had gone into the red in 1965, and the reduced six percent dividend had to be paid from reserves. Although attempts were made to calm the market through occasional sales, the price still rose from 240 to 360 during the latter half of 1966. The Germans and, indeed, the NSU board were mystified. Daimler-Benz, British Motor Corporation, Curtiss-Wright, and Chrysler were all suspected at one time or another of being the buyers. They all denied the idea.

Another possible buyer of shares turned out to be a red herring. Dr. Albers, the champion of the small shareholders who owned about an eighth of the NSU equity, received a letter from New York. It ha‿ a faint postmark labeled "EC Consultants" and offered the membe ‿s of his small shareholders' league a price of DM 500 a share for thei stocks. The selling price naturally moved to over DM 400, but then died down again. Only at that point was it discovered that the source of the letter was a small stockbroking firm, which denied they had a client and which was clearly operating only as a personal speculation, not as a front for a major organization.

Not until early 1968 did the IBB break its cover. By that time, NSU and Citroen had agreed on the first stages of Bunford's plan. NSU was to increase its share capital by DM 35 million to DM 100 million. But only DM 6.5 million of the increase would be allocated to existing shareholders. Citroen would take up the remaining DM 28.5 million, giving it one percent of the NSU equity for every DM 1 million it subscribed, and the controlling 28.5 percent could be increased to a majority by buying in the market. It was reported that Citroen was prepared to pay only DM 300 a share, but NSU wanted 400—then the market price.

The companies were already linked through Comotor, and plans were made for an engine factory to supply both companies. It was to be in the Saar, an area that had been the cockpit of Franco-German rivalry for a thousand years. In addition to the symbolic value of the proposed factory's location, the provincial government of the Saar was anxious to find work for miners being displaced by the decline of its coal mines and was prepared to give generous infrastructure grants of around $5 million to help get the enterprise going. At the same time, Citroen's GS car, designed for a rotary as well as a conventional engine, was nearing the production stage.

But in the middle of 1967, Nordhoff resigned, a dying man. His successor, Kurt Lotz, who had previously run the German branch of the Swiss Brown Bovari electrical company, was totally unfamiliar with the auto industry. He had neither the authority nor the willingness to push through any merger with Citroen. At this point, the IBB intervened. The bank objected strongly to the terms of the deal with Citroen and told NSU as much. The Dresdner Bank threatened the IBB's Swiss bankers, the mighty Union Bank of Switzerland (UBS), that if UBS continued to act for the Israelis, the

Dresdner would boycott the Swiss. But the Swiss banker neutrally replied that the Israelis were good customers of the Union Bank and that they could find other bankers to act for them if the UBS did not.

By this time, Dr. Richter found himself playing an increasingly uncomfortable double role. As chairman of NSU, he had agreed to the deal with Citroen. As a member of the supervisory board of Volkswagen, he was naturally worried at the foreign menace represented by Citroen's growing influence on NSU. The foreign threat grew even more alarming later in 1968 when the Michelin family announced its intention of selling a major stake in Citroen to the Italian Fiat company. For Fiat had that year overtaken VW to become the biggest auto manufacturer in Europe, and after the Fiat-Citroen deal it was certain that the Germans would not allow foreign interests to take over any of their auto companies.

Von Heydekampf had, in theory anyway, been given a free hand by the NSU board to find a German partner for his company. Lotz was an obvious choice, and early in 1969 von Heydekampf found what seemed an appropriate formula for a takeover. VW would not itself take over NSU, but, in a deal similar in some ways to the abortive arrangement with Citroen, NSU itself would be the nominal bidder, in this case for one of VW's subsidiaries, Audi Auto-Union. This company would be allocated DM 130 million in NSU shares, giving VW (as Audi Auto-Union's owners) a sixty-percent stake in NSU.

This arrangement had a number of advantages from VW's point of view. VW would not have to get permission from its own shareholders, who included the federal and provincial governments. It would not involve VW in any cash payment to the existing shareholders in NSU, who would be reduced to a forty-percent rump in the combined company.

VW would also get control of a vital NSU development. This was not the rotary, let alone the unreliable RO80, but a still unproduced design, the K70, a handsome, middle-priced, front-wheel-drive car designed like the Citroen GS, that could be fitted with either a rotary or orthodox engine. NSU was due to produce the K70 during 1969, and it would have provided lethal competition to the 411, VW's belated and uninspired attempt to repeat the success of the Beetle in a bigger car. VW badly needed the K70 and indeed produced and sold it after the merger, though not under the NSU label.

NSU's shareholders knew all this and also that whereas their dividend had never been more than eight percent, VW regularly paid twenty percent—the dividend NSU shareholders would have received if VW had paid for NSU in its own shares. Using the shares of its Auto-Union subsidiary to buy NSU enabled Lotz to avoid paying out an increased dividend to the former NSU shareholders.

Von Heydekampf and Lotz agreed on terms in the middle of February, and in the last week of the month, Lotz publicly admitted that a merger was indeed under way. The NSU shares promptly shot up by a fifth in a few days, and during the week after the announcement, they bounced around between 610 and 660. Lotz and von Heydekampf had hoped to disarm opposition to the deal by an offer which the NSU chief executive described as "so attractive that there will be no opposition on the part of the shareholders." The sweetener concerned the rights to the income from the Wankel engine. This would be separated from the rest of NSU's business, and existing NSU shareholders would be allotted "genusscheine"—participating warrants—which would give them some share in the profits from the Wankel engine. (The exact amount was not divulged until later.)

After the announcement of the deal, the stock market promptly went mad and started to buy and sell what were, in effect, nonexistent bits of paper of totally unknown value. Until the stock market's authorities stopped the trading in them, the genusscheine were selling on the stock market at around DM 180 apiece—even though they did not exist, the company they were attached to was not yet in being, and the price therefore a complete fantasy. But the market was still besotted with the rotary dream. The price of 600 for the NSU shares was itself completely unrealistic, even if all the outstanding licensees had gone immediately into full-scale production. The genusscheine were indeed extraordinary; for they expressed in hard cash the purely visionary value of the invention itself uncomplicated by manufacturers' costs, management, and other irrelevancies.

The actual terms of profit sharing proposed then, however, were far worse than the market had supposed, and, by any criterion, were bad enough to prompt a real uproar among NSU stockholders. The genusscheine were to get only two-fifths of the income from the Wankel and that only for ten years. There was no mention of any compensation to existing NSU shareholders for the costs of developing the K70 which, it was clear by then, was an important part of the takeover. Yet NSU had developed the car with its own money, and VW would get the majority of the profits from it. Nor was there any indication that VW would have to pay any royalties to the holders of the genusscheine if it used the Wankel engine in any of its cars.

IBB inevitably returned to the fray. By then the bank had accumulated over ten percent of the shares and, by advertising their opposition in the German press, had got the proxy support of another fifteen or more percent—enough to give them the twenty-five percent needed to block any move by a company under German law. The IBB sent their Israeli lawyer, Elihu Miron, and a director, Joshua Bension, to negotiate. The pair were indeed unlikely adversaries for the might of the German industrial establishment, as were the shareholders they represented.° Bension, the son-in-law of IBB's chairman, small, amiable, eager, bouncy, was the front man. But the real strength of the team was Miron. Sallow, lean, cadaverous, melancholy, and orthodox in his religious observances, he had the invaluable lawyer's habit of reading every document carefully. He was also a natural litigant prepared to go to court whenever there was any hitch in negotiations—and he experienced many during the next five years.

With their German lawyer, Lois Erdl, they went to see the VW management, claiming to represent twenty-five percent of the equity.

They immediately put forward six key points—and demanded satisfaction on all of them. Only then would the votes they represented be cast in favor of the arrangement with Auto-Union at the special meeting which had been called for the purpose in April 1969. The IBB's demands included lengthening the life of the genusscheine to fifteen years, increasing the percentage of the royalty income they would receive from two-fifths to two-thirds, ensuring that VW would pay a royalty if it made Wankel-engined cars, compensating the NSU shareholders for the costs incurred in developing the K70, and ensuring that the rights of the genusscheine could not be taken away. VW refused to discuss the matter, assuming that the IBB represented

---

° These included the German subsidiary of Bernie Cornfield's mutual fund empire, Investors Overseas Services (IOS). Miron had been IOS's lawyer in Israel, hence the purchase—one of the very few profitable ones made by IOS.

only a small percent of the equity. (Dissenters to a company's policy often represented only a fraction of the shareholding they claimed.) VW decided to call the IBB's bluff and wait for the alleged proxies to arrive.

Next day Miron and Bension dispatched a first batch of proxies, representing over ten percent of the equity, from Erdl's Munich office, with indications that more would be forthcoming. VW promptly gave way, and the Israelis were asked to send a telex setting out the six points they insisted on. At a further meeting in Düsseldorf, VW agreed to the IBB's terms—but with one significant alteration: The NSU shareholders were to be compensated for the development costs of the K70, but only those incurred up to December 31, 1968. Since a great chunk of the total expenditure had been incurred in the last few months, when spending on preproduction tooling was at its height, this modification saved VW millons.

Miron and Bension had the offending clause removed and then managed to get VW to agree on what questions IBB would ask—and the replies they wanted the VW representatives to make—at the Extraordinary General Meeting, that would explain the six points and ensure there would be no going back on them.

The meeting was held on April 26, 1969, in the empty production bay which was to have been the assembly line for the K70. (It was promptly dubbed the K70 memorial hall.) About a thousand shareholders turned up, including Wankel himself, who went unrecognized in the crowd.

The mood of the meeting was ugly. There were complaints about the name proposed for the combined company, Audi-NSU-Auto-Union. There were charges against the big banks—not just the Dresdner but the Deutsche Bank as well—that they had claimed to be dispensing impartial advice although, in fact, they had a vested interest in the deal.

The shareholders felt strongly that the banks and VW were presenting the shareholders with a fait accompli and were determined to block the deal if they could. However, when the terms of the IBB-VW agreement were announced, most of the opposition died down. Even then there was an uproar from a few die-hard opponents of the deal. One shareholder, Kurt Fiebich, remarked that there must be a VW man lurking somewhere in the room. At that moment, the blue curtain behind the supervisory board parted, and out stepped Dr. Prinz, a member of the VW board. There was a hush; then someone made a motion that Prinz, as a representative of another company, should not address an NSU shareholders' meeting. Speaking from the microphone used by ordinary shareholders, Prinz told the meeting, "I hope that you will spare me from commenting on the accusations made against VW."

Eighteen months later the first annual meeting of the combined company, Audi-NSU-Auto-Union, was even more chaotic. It was also the longest meeting in German corporate history, lasting twenty-six hours and forty-one minutes, with 500 shareholders attending. Lotz, the chairman of the combined company, was determined to allow all the critics to have their say. Besides making and listening to speeches, the stockholders consumed 2,000 sausages, 670 bread rolls, 3,000 plates of soup, 1,200 cups of coffee, and 5,000 bottles of soft drinks.

At the meeting, dissident shareholders accused Lotz of trying, with the connivance of the Dresdner Bank, to mop up the outstanding shares of NSU on the cheap. The bank had already given him an option on their seventeen-percent holding at an inflated price of DM 130 million.

He was also accused of having misled the shareholders in the original deal between NSU and the VW subsidiary, Audi Auto-Union, by inserting a clause never made public. According to this clause, the subsidiary had to pay a substantial annual fee to VW (in 1969, it was DM 15 million). The payment was to compensate VW for the alleged economic and organizational advantages Audi Auto-Union had gained in the takeover. It also represented tax-free income from its subsidiary. Had the same money been paid as a dividend on Audi-NSU-Auto-Union stocks, it would have been taxed. The clause exposed the management of Audi Auto-Union as simply subordinate executives who worked for Lotz and in no position to defend their shareholders' interests.

Lotz had not even told von Heydekampf or the NSU board of the deal. At the meeting he claimed, unconvincingly, that he had sent the relevant documents, but they had been lost in the post. The shareholders—wrongly but naturally—assumed that von Heydekampf was in league with VW. Out of loyalty to VW, he did not refute the assumption—though his wife confessed that at several points during the twenty-six hours of the meeting, she nearly burst out with the truth to shield her husband from the unjust accusation made against him.

Lotz's offer—in VW shares—for the remaining NSU shares was derisory. "The worst that has ever been presented in German history," according to Dr. Albers. They were a mere seventy percent of par (DM 100). This was well below the figure the Dresdner Bank had demanded for its shares or the price VW had paid in the market for the additional shares needed to bring its shareholding above seventy-five percent—the crucial level at which VW was automatically entitled under German law to make an offer for the remaining shares. Lotz, not unexpectedly, was accused of "neglecting his duty," of "making a gross attempt at deception," "lying," and he received a Teutonic insult best rendered as "primitive turnover-thinking," which means that he cared about his company's sales rather than its profits.

One result of this meeting was that Miron and IBB went to court. Miron obtained injunctions in two lower courts, enjoining VW to suspend the takeover contract on the grounds that Lotz had clearly broken the undertaking—given at the time of the merger—that NSU would retain its independence. Consequently, the IBB became a sort of hero in the German press. Asked one paper, "Do we have to have the Israelis to defend German shareholders?"

The IBB outlasted Lotz, whose "pure domination mentality," as it was described, proved too much for his colleagues. He was replaced in 1971 by the former boss of Audi, Rudolf Leiding, who also inherited the row with IBB and the other minority shareholders. In the end, after a marathon late-night negotiating session lasting ten hours, the Israelis, acting for their own fourteen percent of the equity and the rest of the minority, accepted a price of DM 226, three times Lotz's original offer. By that time, VW's need for NSU's skills, ideas, and designs had become abundantly clear. The K70 was being produced by the combined firm, and many of NSU's best engineers and management had been drafted to help VW at Wolfsburg to catch up with other European motor manufacturers and find designs to replace the faithful but aging Beetle.

The genusscheine survived the three-year battle unscathed. They are still being briskly traded, still overvalued by normal investment rules because of the continuing glamor of the Wankel name. Comotor also survived.

By tacit agreement, Citroen was allowed to run the company, even though the share split between NSU and the French company remained equal. In the autumn of 1973, three years later, Citroen finally announced its version of the GS with rotary engine based on the RO80 unit. By that time, Comotor had been provided with a proper separate management, headed by Marc Picquet, a tough and practical production executive.

But Picquet, like so many executives in the Wankel history, was helpless in the grip of business politics. Today, almost a year after Citroen's announcement, he has his splendid new factory, crisp and modern in its pleasant rural setting, still waiting for the machinery to enable it to produce the 1,000 engines a day of which it is capable. But he is dependent on the plans of VW and Citroen. Judging by past form, the French company ought to be his best potential customer. But the outlook is totally unclear.

A whole family of engines—of one and two rotors—is being developed by at least three development teams, at NSU, at Citroen, and at Comotor itself. But the outlook within Citroen is now clouded. There was always an anti-Wankel element within the company even during the height of Bercot's power—engineers who could never reconcile themselves to accepting ideas from outside. They are likely to be reinforced in their prejudices since Citroen's forced merger in 1974 with Peugeot, its long-standing rival. And the terms of the merger make it quite clear that Peugeot—whose management has never shown the slightest interest in the Wankel—will run the combined company.

On the other hand, the Peugeot management might be converted to the Wankel cause as thoroughly and as surprisingly as two successive chairmen of VW have been. Lotz had never been a Wankel enthusiast. But in 1971, just before he was deposed, he visited Toyo Kogyo at Hiroshima and came away transformed—declaring that "Neckarsulm is going to be the Wankel center of the world."

Leiding, his successor, started off by canceling the plans to equip the Audi 100, a very successful family sedan, with a rotary engine. He explained, "We have not always been happy with the Wankel engine. It had defective seals, cost millions in guarantee payments, and gave our competitors the chance to try better designs."

A subordinate added loyally, "We throw a few thousand marks after every RO80 we sell." But Leiding soon saw the light. For two weeks in the summer of 1974, he tried out a new VW luxury car with one of the bigger two-rotor engines developed for Comotor by the NSU engineers. He was starry-eyed as a result. Every day with the car, he said, "was like a honeymoon."

11

*Tiny and
the "Mittelmen"*

"He claimed that on no less than four separate occasions
between August 9 and October 20, 1971, Mr. Rowland
misinformed or allowed the board to be misinformed on the true
cost and nature of the Wankel purchase."
  —Counsel for William Wilkinson, former director of Lonrho

NSU owned only sixty percent of the Wankel business. Wankel
G.m.B.h., the private company owned jointly by Wankel and Hutzenlaub, held the minority forty percent shareholding in the rights,
and, naturally, there was as much interest in Wankel G.m.B.h. as in
NSU. Moreover, by 1969, both partners in Wankel G.m.B.h. were
willing sellers. Hutzenlaub indeed had grown noisily skeptical of the
allegedly unique virtues of the engine out of which he had made so
much money. He felt that it would work only as a "hybrid" unit,
driving a generator in conjunction with an electric motor. The rights
were offered to so many German companies that the story was
becoming "stale beer," in the words of one auto industry executive.

Fortunately for Wankel and Hutzenlaub, a number of non-Ger-
mans were interested. Bunford was eager; he offered DM 40 million
for the company in 1968; and the IBB was also interested. But the
eventual and improbable winner, in the battle for the forty percent,
was London and Rhodesian Estates (Lonrho), a British trading and
mining company whose interests were almost exclusively in Africa.
Its chief executive was a controversial six-foot-three-inch charmer,
Roland Rowland, known universally as "Tiny."

117

According to his own account, he was born in Calcutta, of a British mother and a German father who had been at one time the financial adviser to the Dalai Lama. During World War II, Tiny's father was interned in Britain as an enemy alien, and Tiny found himself at the end of the war forced to work as a railway porter at a London main-line station. Legend has it that he made a good living by getting the signalmen in the box just outside the station to tell him where the first-class carriages would stop, thereby ensuring he carried only the more affluent passengers' baggage.

His business history begins in the 1950s in what was then Southern Rhodesia (today known as Rhodesia). He was a chauffeur and a farmer, before acquiring the franchise for Mercedes-Benz cars. He also worked for the giant mining house Rio-Tinto Zinc (RTZ), with whom his relationship has always been close but ambiguous. "He produced business for us, but was not in our employ" is the careful RTZ description.

At the turn of the decade, he sold his auto distribution business to a small British public company, London and Rhodesian Estates (Lonrho for short), in exchange for enough shares to effectively make him the director of the company's destiny. In the next decade, he transformed Lonrho from a sleepy colonial concern into the biggest trading company in Africa and one of the most-talked-about conglomerates on the London stock market.

Tiny had the genius to take advantage of the simple fact that when countries in black Africa gained their independence, the stock market values of companies with interests there slumped.

Tiny grabbed his chance to buy cheap: Motor distributors in Kenya, gold mines in Ghana, cotton mills in Nigeria all came into the Lonrho net. Tiny himself tirelessly crisscrossed Africa in the Lonrho jet, asking, as he landed in a new country, "What's for sale here?" He would turn his rugged, handsome face, his blankly penetrating blue eyes, his formidable charm, his lean, impressive, well-tailored appearance, his slightly drawling, impeccable English to work on the leaders of these countries and establish close personal relationships with many of them.

In the eyes of an observer as unimpressionable as Sir Roy Welensky, Rhodesia's former prime minister, he was "the best thing to hit Africa since Cecil Rhodes"—the legendary Englishman who had built up the De Beers diamond monopoly in the last years of the nineteenth century. In business terms he had increased Lonrho's profits from under $500,000 in 1961 to over $35 million ten years later. He had also attracted a formidable crowd of enemies. For example, much of South Africa's business establishment hated him. They said it was because they knew too much about his early business dealings in Rhodesia and some of the methods he employed. His supporters said merely that the South Africans hated Lonrho's success, which proved it was possible to do profitable business in black Africa. By then, too, the City of London was concerned about his freewheeling one-man style of business. He had built up Lonrho by taking over well-established businesses, which he then left alone. Even his friends do not claim he is a manager, and his enemies say he is a compulsive wheeler and dealer, incapable of running an on-going group.

By the end of the sixties, he was trying to build up new businesses, not swallow existing ones. It had always been his dream to emulate the enormous mining groups like Harry Oppenheimer's South African-based Anglo-American, which operated on a worldwide basis. Among other enterprises, Tiny helped to finance a massive new platinum mine in South Africa, and planned—fruitlessly—to build an ambitious new railway system in Zaire, formerly the Belgian Congo.

A man like Tiny, with limitless charm and vision, who saw no boundaries, geographical or technical, to his business ambitions, was precisely the sort of executive—like Roy Hurley before him—who was naturally attracted to the Wankel.

Tiny first heard about the company from another charmer of Middle-European origins, Stefan Klein. Born in Austria, Klein came to Britain originally in the 1930s to try to sell the rights to an Austrian-designed autogiro, an unsuccessful predecessor of the helicopter. He had first met Tiny while he was running a hotel in Nairobi, and they had subsequently worked together on various deals. Klein, who commutes between London, Munich, and a holiday home on Corfu, heard that the rights of Wankel G.m.B.h. were for sale through a Munich lawyer, Rolf Hansen, engaged by Hutzenlaub to help sell the companies.

There were *two* companies involved, and two sets of people selling them. By 1969, three-quarters of the money received by Wankel g.m.b.h. that came from license fees and royalties from non-German sources never came into Germany at all. It was channeled through another company, Rotary Engines, set up by Wankel and Hutzenlaub in Switzerland, where Hutzenlaub lives much of the time and Wankel has a house. Rotary Engines pays for any research done by third parties. It was obviously convenient to pay for this from money that had not been subject to German taxation.

In effect, then, there were two companies for sale, with—more confusingly—several people simultaneously selling them. Hutzenlaub was, in theory, acting for Wankel as well as for himself. In practice, Rolf Hansen, Hutzenlaub's Munich lawyer, was also on the lookout for buyers, and Wankel, suspicious of his old partner, had acquired his own agent. A rich Swiss arms salesman, Dr. Adolf Gerber, an old friend of Wankel's and a rotary enthusiast, had turned up at Lindau one day in a Porsche sports car adapted to take a rotary engine and had promptly been hired to run Wankel G.m.B.h. and Rotary Engines, whose previous manager, a Swiss engineer called Leo Wyrsch, had, like so many others, quarreled with Wankel.

But Gerber did not take control and start acting officially for Wankel as a check on Hutzenlaub's activities immediately. Until 1970, Hutzenlaub was running Wankel G.m.B.h. and, in theory, acting for both Wankel and himself. During 1968, in fact, he had come to a provisional understanding with Max Bunford to sell both companies for DM 40 million.

The next year Klein heard about the opportunity to buy Wankel G.m.B.h. from Hansen. Naturally, he told his old friend Tiny. Klein claims that he sold a previously ignorant Tiny on the advantages of the engine during a ride in an RO80; Tiny says, on the other hand, that he had followed the Wankel's progress from its early days because of a continuing interest in the auto industry derived from his distributorships in Africa. Whatever the truth, Tiny found the ride smoother than in his habitual Rolls-Royce, and it only took him half an hour to decide to "buy the fucking thing," according to Klein.

However, it took nearly three years to translate this snap decision into practice. Tiny's first idea was to form a consortium of Lonrho, his old partner RTZ, and the only major British-owned motor group, British Leyland. But the British company was never very eager, and even the partnership with RTZ faltered. One reason was that during 1970, the price demanded for Wankel G.m.B.h. escalated as new bidders emerged.

In 1970, the first new bidder was the IBB, which reached an agreement with Hutzenlaub to buy a quarter of the company—valuing the whole concern at DM 80 million. Hutzenlaub signed up and allegedly promised to get Wankel's signature as well. He did not succeed, or maybe he did not even try (the matter is still the subject of litigation). For in early 1970, General Motors intervened. The Americans wanted to buy Wankel G.m.B.h.—at a suggested price of DM 90 million—rather than take out a license to make the engine. But GM had to withdraw from the negotiations after realizing that buying the Wankel company would almost certainly have incurred the wrath of the U.S. antitrust authorities. At that time they were in active pursuit of the corporation and had already broken up an attempt by it and the other major auto companies to work together on antipollution devices. GM's interest did have the effect of whetting Hutzenlaub's appetite, and the price for Wankel G.m.B.h. started to escalate.

At the same time, Tiny's ideas were growing even more elaborate. Early in 1971, Rolls-Royce declared bankruptcy, and its Automobile and Diesel Engine Division came up for sale. Tiny's fertile mind jumped at the chance of combining the Wankel firm with Rolls-Royce, maker of the world's finest cars, and the only company that had used Wankel's principles to design and build a practicable rotary diesel engine. Like the proposed partnership with RTZ, this idea also came to nothing.

Undiscouraged, early in 1971 Tiny flew with Klein in the Lonrho private jet on a day trip to Bad Gastein, a spa in the Austrian Alps, where Bunford spends a fortnight every year taking the cure (he retains shrapnel fragments in his body from the war). Bunford and Tiny agreed that they should make a joint offer of DM 80 million for the company. But this price assumed that a solution could be found to a number of outstanding problems, including minimizing the German tax Wankel and Hutzenlaub would have to pay for any development work carried out at Wankel's institute. Finally, it would incorporate Wankel's share of the $50 million eventually due from the GM license agreement signed the previous December—a sum reckoned at $10 million or more.

But this deal depended on the agreement of the IBB, because of its previous agreement with Hutzenlaub, and of Karl Kahane, a Swiss banker who had acted as intermediary for Bunford and the IBB.

Klein himself had been offered a commission of $500,000, but preferred to take a share of the equity. So Tiny, Bunford, and Klein flew off on another one-day trip in the Lonrho jet, this time to Tel Aviv. By this time Tiny had decided, as he told Klein, that if he could not beat the opposition he had better join it.

In Tel Aviv, Tiny, Bunford, Kahane, and the IBB agreed that Wankel G.m.B.h. would be split three ways, half to Lonrho, and a quarter each to Bunford and the IBB. But once Tiny had begun negotiations with Hutzenlaub, the price escalated further. Hutzenlaub declared that the only fair way to value the income from the Wankel company was on the same rate as the stock market was valuing the genusscheine. The income involved was indeed from the same source—royalties and license fees from the engine. But the stock market was always more than generous toward any stock connected with the Wankel engine; so any price for Wankel G.m.B.h. based on the value of the genusscheine was inevitably an inflated one.

Hutzenlaub's asking price had now escalated to DM 150 million (he claimed that on a strict comparison with the genusscheine, the price should have been DM 200 million). After several months of haggling, Tiny agreed in August to buy the rights for DM 100 million. This was more than his partners had bargained for, and they were reluctant to pay their share (though Bunford claims that he, at least, had the money more readily available than Tiny himself).

Tiny's persuasive powers were strong enough to talk his partners into surrendering their rights in return for a relatively small percentage of shares in the company. The plum he offered was that Lonrho would pay the whole DM 100 million purchase price. Klein, Kahane, Bunford, and the IBB would each get five percent of the company free, but would surrender any legal claims they might have made against Lonrho. Bunford then took options from Kahane and Klein to bring his potential holding up to fifteen percent.

The minority shareholders secured special voting rights to ensure that the company was managed as a proper industrial enterprise. Gerber was by now Wankel's general manager, and, immediately after signing the agreement on behalf of Wankel's company, he joined Lonrho as a director and as manager of the Wankel business.

To simplify the tax position, Hutzenlaub drew up a contract which provided for only DM 64 million to be paid. This was the down payment fixed in the settlement Tiny had suggested. The remaining DM 36 million was to be paid from General Motors' annual license payments. But this DM 36 million was not mentioned in either of two new agreements drafted that autumn. Removing it from the legal agreement reduced Wankel and Hutzenlaub's liability to tax on their capital gain from the sale of Wankel G.m.B.h., although it was clearly understood by all the parties actually engaged in the negotiations that the remaining money would indeed be paid. The fact that this was nowhere stated in the documents could—and did—prove a cause for misunderstanding. By this time, the end of 1970, the autocratic Tiny was in all sorts of trouble with his colleagues on the Lonrho board. Even before the negotiations started, Lonrho had been facing a liquidity crisis because of Tiny's freewheeling and seemingly compulsive acquisitions policy. Going ahead independently with the Wankel negotiations following RTZ's withdrawal proved too much for Lonrho's then financial advisers, S. G. Warburg, the well-respected merchant bank. As a direct result of the shortage of cash, the Lonrho board had to be strengthened by a number of independent directors, headed by Sir Basil Smallpeice, a former chairman of the Cunard shipping group (and later, an adviser on business management to the British Royal Household). The appointment of these new directors, it was assumed, would ensure that Tiny changed his ways and acted as a member of a properly organized team. For as a special accountant's report put it later, the existing management organization of Lonrho "was now unsuitable for administering the complex and diversified group which Lonrho had become."

As the negotiations continued during 1971, some of the directors grew increasingly incensed. They felt, as one of them later testified, that "all in all, Mr. Rowland treats Lonrho as a private fief, although he holds only twenty percent of the equity."

This accusation comes from a court action taken two years later by Tiny at which the whole convoluted story came into the open. Eight dissident directors, led by Smallpeice and backed by the whole weight of respectable City of London opinion, had tried to sack Tiny. He had responded by calling for an extraordinary general meeting of shareholders because he was convinced that the small investors in Lonrho would be loyal to him, and that loyalty, combined with his personal holding, would defeat the rebels. But he was forced to take legal action to restrain the board from dismissing him *before* the meeting could be convened.

In his evidence in the ensuing court case, William Wilkinson, a merchant banker who had been brought in at the same time as Smallpeice, testified that the board had assumed that Lonrho would pay only DM 64 million for 100 percent of the Wankel companies, whereas the total agreed payment was of course DM 100 million— and twenty percent was to be allocated to the minority holders.

According to Wilkinson's lawyer, Tiny

had invited Wilkinson to report on the Wankel matter to the full board. Mr. Wilkinson had done so in good faith on what Mr. Rowland had told him. What the board was told had been wholly and utterly misleading, and Mr. Rowland had sat silently by while the board approved a travesty of the true deal that he was making.

The meeting referred to was on August 9, 1971, and specifically only authorized Tiny to buy 100 percent of the companies for DM 64 million. But the next day, another meeting of the full board authorized Tiny to negotiate and vary the terms "in his absolute discretion," a loophole which allowed Tiny to increase the price and reduce the percentage. A few days later, the *Wall Street Journal* reported that Lonrho was to acquire Wankel g.m.b.h. at a price reported to be "in the region" of $33 million—over DM 120 million at the then exchange rate.

At the trial, Tiny was charged with having "misled the board on four separate occasions as to the true cost and nature of the Wankel purchase." This charge referred to a series of board meetings during the summer at which the price was assumed (by Wilkinson anyway) to be only DM 64 million. Wilkinson claimed that he learned about the commitment to pay the additional DM 36 million only in September. He was then, he alleged, assured that the extra money would be paid personally by Tiny.

"I am," he added, "particularly clear on this point because, at a later stage, Mr. Rowland said to me that if he died, the liability would fall on his estate."

To his horror Wilkinson then discovered that "this payment was not a personal commitment of Mr. Rowland at all, but rather an additional liability on Lonrho." But even in September he had not grasped the full details of the purchase.

Only a month later, "on or about October 15, I heard from an associate of Rowland that Rowland had undertaken to grant, free of charge, a minority interest in Wankel G.m.B.h. to a group of outsiders for certain services."

Tiny claimed that the full scheme was made clear in various papers available to Wilkinson. But the negotiations and documents were in German, a language which only Tiny Rowland and one other director spoke fluently. Whether Tiny had concealed the truth or whether Wilkinson could have read all about the deal—albeit in a language with which he was only imperfectly familiar—is still unclear. At the time he, and the rest of the Lonrho board, had other and more urgent problems to worry about. For in October—the same month in which, Wilkinson claimed, he first appreciated the full extent of Tiny's dealings—the South African police arrested a number of the company's senior executives, including one main board director, and charged them with fraud, and two of the most respected Lonrho directors resigned.

Nevertheless, the deal for Wankel g.m.b.h. had gone ahead. A fourth and supposedly final agreement was reached in January 1972. As before, the IBB, Bunford, Klein, and Kahane were to get twenty percent of the equity. The purchase price was DM 100 million, which Wilkinson had managed to raise at the advantageous rate of seven and a half percent from the Union Bank of Switzerland.

By this time, the artificial division between the DM 64 million contract and the additional payment outside Germany had had to be abandoned, for the German tax authorities had got wind of the changes in the terms and the attempt to pay the additional DM 36 million tax free—which they naturally intimated they would block. But this was not the only change made in the January 1972 contract, and all the other alterations in the terms markedly favored Wankel and Hutzenlaub.

Payment was to be made much more quickly. In the first contract, the final DM 36 million was to be paid from GM's license revenues—in six installments up to 1975. In the final agreement, the new owners were to pay the DM 36 million within two years. In the early agreement, the buyers had not inherited any of the personal charges on the company. But in the final settlement, Lonrho found itself liable for the substantial golden handshake awarded to Wyrsch, the sacked former manager of Rotary Engines; the payment of the two percent of the revenue due to be paid to Frau Hoeppner, the widow of Wankel's chief designer; payments for two lawyers—and a pension for Wankel himself. Lonrho also had to pay everyone's legal costs.

There was further bickering even after this supposedly final agreement; in a sworn affidavit filed in the case involving Rowland and his dissident directors, Hutzenlaub testified that at a subsequent meeting in January 1972 (when Gerber was supposed to be acting on Lonrho's behalf), Gerber had said he

would do everything to extract the sum of DM 12 million from Lonrho and asked me what he would get for this. When I asked him what he had in mind, he suggested a commission of ten percent. Dr. Gerber wished to have the commission paid immediately, which I refused, saying that I would pay the commission only after we had received the money.

Gerber tried to increase the purchase price at a meeting at the end of the same month. But Tiny was furious and claimed that he "would never have made such a promise without the consent of the board" and that Gerber must have misunderstood if he thought there was any suggestion of DM 12 million more being paid.

In May 1973, Gerber and the seven other directors hostile to Tiny were removed from the Lonrho board, thanks to Tiny's substantial personal stake in Lonrho and his success in rallying small shareholders to his side at the extraordinary general meeting. But there are still a number of lawsuits outstanding. Frau Hoeppner is suing because she is being paid only on the royalties from the sale of engines and not, also, the percentage on license down payments to which she feels herself entitled. Until it went bankrupt, the IBB was suing Wankel and Hutzenlaub personally for allegedly breaking the option agreement by which the IBB was to have twenty-five percent of their company for DM 18 million. Wankel and Hutzenlaub are also being sued by Fred Oppenheimer because, he claims, he was never properly compensated by them for giving up his right to market rotary cars in the United States. In his turn, Hutzenlaub is suing Lonrho to reclaim DM 4.5 million in back royalties and license fees he claims are due to him and not the new owners of Wankel G.m.B.h., because they were earned before the company was sold.

More serious than these legal loose ends is that Wankel G.m.B.h. has remained purely a revenue-collection business since Lonrho acquired it. It has no independent management and has not even been commissioning the research work from Felix Wankel to which it was entitled. There were some desultory discussions with Ricardo, the famous British diesel engine research firm, which was anxious to work on the rotary, but the idea was dropped.

This passive role is very far from the one company envisaged by both the IBB and Bunford. They wanted to use Wankel G.m.B.h. as a central clearinghouse of rotary research and as a promotional organization for the whole rotary idea. As such it would have been invaluable during the great anti-Wankel hysteria described in Chapter 21.

But Tiny is no industrialist. His attitude is that IBB and Bunford are merely trying to spend his money, and any chief executive, he feels, would have found it impossible to work with the disputatious Henn. His own plans for Wankel G.m.B.h. are, characteristically, both vague and ambitious. He would like to combine the two major license holders, Curtiss-Wright and Wankel G.m.B.h., in some way, preferably bringing in Audi-NSU and Comotor as well, to provide one center for the rotary business. He might even manage it, but rotary enthusiasts are fortunate that the progress of their favorite engine does not depend on him, but has found more practical supporters in other industries and other countries.

12

Enter Mr. Matsuda

"We are a nation of gamblers."
—Tsuneji Matsuda, chairman of Toyo Kogyo

The license agreement with Toyo Kogyo, which Henn negotiated in the autumn of 1963, unexpectedly provided the engine with its best ally up to that stage in its history.

Toyo Kogyo was a superficially not very promising recruit. In the early 1960s, virtually all its production was in small cars and trucks, mostly three-wheelers and a mere 360 cc. But like NSU and Curtiss-Wright, it had a chief executive with vision and a desire for immortality and an engineer to make the rotary work. Von Heydekampf had had Froede, and Hurley had had Max Bentele. The Japanese team consisted of Tsuneji Matsuda and Kenichi Yamamoto. Toyo Kogyo, like NSU at the time of the Wankel's arrival, was just emerging from the production of purely utilitarian means of transport suitable for the austere times both Japan and Germany were enduring in the 1950s. Neither company, as a consequence, had to fight inherited tradition. Neither company was saddled with expensive machinery already at work making medium- or large-sized reciprocating engines—a situation that would have acted as a cautionary brake on any rotary plans.

Toyo Kogyo had two major advantages over both NSU and Curtiss-Wright: It was a family firm, and it was already financially successful. There was no danger that shareholders or directors would rise in revolt against the ambitious long-term plans of a visionary chief executive, as in the case of Curtiss-Wright and Hurley. And unlike von Heydekampf, Matsuda did not feel that if he failed to produce a successful rotary engine quickly, the independence of the firm was in danger.

Tsuneji Matsuda—in Japanese his last name means "pine-field"—fitted perfectly into the Hurley mold. He liked to think of himself as a self-made man, "like Henry Ford and Lord Nuffield." He used to boast, "I started from nothing." In fact, he received a sound technical engineering education at the local high school, but his vision of himself was all of a piece with the role he deliberately adopted throughout his career—the outsider, the man prepared to think and act differently from other people in the same industry.

Matsuda, in fact, did not have to start from nothing. His father had started in business on his own in 1920, first making cork products—the name Toyo Kogyo means "oriental cork"—then, like Lord Nuffield, bicycles. His company claims to have made the first motorized cycles in Japan.

In 1931, six years before Mr. Toyoda made his first Toyota car, their firm made the first handful of cars (they were only three-wheelers) built in Japan. The car was called a Mazda, from the family name. By 1940, the Matsudas were selling 1,500 three-wheelers a year and were about to market their first four-wheeled vehicle when the war intervened.

Toyo Kogyo's headquarters and factory were (and still are) three miles outside Hiroshima, on the coastline of Japan's inland sea and separated from the town by low hills. This site proved providential when the atom bomb was dropped on the town, on August 6, 1945. The hills shielded the factory from any damage more severe than broken glass and collapsed roofs. Virtually no one was hurt.

"Only absentee employees were killed that day," Matsuda recalled later.

Although after the war the factory was stripped for reparations, by 1947 Matsuda had started up again, using steel from surplus war stock. By the late 1950s, it had become probably the most advanced producer of vehicles in Japan. Tsuneji had by then been joined by his son Kohei, who took over as chief executive on his father's death in 1970. They embarked on a typically flamboyant expansion scheme. Instead of accepting the limitations of a site hemmed in between the hills and the sea, they built a massive 500-foot bridge with their own money to another piece of land where they built the first properly computer-controlled motor assembly shop outside the United States.

It was capable of producing a greater variety of vehicles on one assembly line than less advanced competitors. Typically, Matsuda even made use of the company's situation on the sea, hundreds of miles from its major markets or its suppliers, as an opportunity to behave differently from other manufacturers. Matsuda built his own fleet of ships and shipped virtually everything—from components to finished cars—by sea, whether they were destined for Japan or foreign countries. As a result, Matsuda boasted that his cars arrived at their destination as bright and shiny as the day they left the factory.

He was also prepared to buck trends in the cars he built. In the early 1960s, his major competitors, Toyota and Nissan, started to build more spacious and refined cars than the small, underpowered vehicles on which all the Japanese manufacturers had previously concentrated. The crucial barrier to bigger engines was the motor tax based on engine capacity. Above 360 cc, it is a significant cost factor.

But until the rotary came along, with its promise of more power in a smaller engine, Matsuda was not to be tempted by the prospect of an increasingly affluent market.

"We feel," he said as late as 1965, "that cars and trucks are basically transportation. They should be sane, sensible, and efficient as can be—at the least possible cost . . . in the words of my advertisements, our vehicles are built sturdily with no unnecessary overhangs and frills."

He recalled he had been told that "people will never buy cars or trucks like yours; they're too strange looking, too small, and haven't enough chrome . . . but we went ahead. People loved our 'sensible' cars so much that nearly 1½ million bought them last year."

When Matsuda bought the license in 1961, he had several advantages over other actual or potential rotary manufacturers. The technical pride and achievement of Toyo Kogyo were based on thoroughness and a willingness to take large risks. The new assembly plant and computerized production line were the obvious examples. His firm was also far more "integrated" than NSU, or, indeed, most non-American auto companies; that is, it made most of its automobiles' components itself. Also, in the 1950s, the Matsudas had imported into Japan the technology for sand-casting small and complicated shapes—like the Wankel's complicated rotor and trochoid housings. And the firm also made many of its own machine tools, a prerequisite for successful rotary manufacturing during the

1960s when the world's machinery manufacturers tended to yawn at the mere mention of the Wankel.

The Matsudas, like almost everyone else, first heard of the engine at the end of 1959, when Hurley broadcast its glories to the world. But it was the Munich symposium in early 1960 that finally convinced them of the feasibility of the idea. The company's official history of the rotary puts it succinctly: "As it was different and much more superior to the rotary engines of the past, it would be possible to put this into practical use." According to the same document, Toyo Kogyo wrote to NSU asking for a license, but was treated somewhat coolly, as befitted an unknown Japanese company at a time when there were plenty of better-known applicants for a license. Allegedly, it was only the happy accident of a visit to the company by Dr. Haas, the German ambassador, in May 1960, when he interceded on behalf of Toyo Kogyo, that enabled the Japanese to get anywhere. What the account leaves out were the energetic efforts being made to sell the license in Japan by NSU's agent, Walter Jensen. In fact, NSU's suspicions were not of Toyo Kogyo in particular, but of the despised Japanese industry in general.

Through the combined efforts of Haas and Jensen, Matsuda and a party of engineers visited NSU in July 1960. They made it clear that they wanted to build their own engines and not be merely an agent for rotary units made by NSU, and within three months an agreement was initialed. It took the Japanese government nine months to bless the deal, a delay which robbed the Matsudas of the honor of being the second licensee, for in the meantime both Fichtel and Sachs, the German manufacturers of small industrial engines, and—through some inexplicable official favoritism—the Japanese Yanmar Diesel, had signed up. According to the company, Toyo Kogyo "did not pay an amazingly high initial payment," but the original agreement covered only sales in Japan.

After a follow-up visit by the Japanese in mid-1961, a KKM 400 engine arrived in Hiroshima on November 1, 1961. The first prototype engine, made by the Japanese entirely from drawings supplied by NSU, began testing at the same time. Within a year it became apparent, to put it mildly, that all was not well with the NSU design. In the company's own words:

This prototype engine, however, showed excessive vibrations at idling speeds, emitted a large amount of white smoke, and its oil consumption was beyond all practical use. When the engine was run for 200 hours, the output suddenly dropped. Upon disassembling the engine, it was found that chatter marks had caused the electroplating to fall off. The results of prototype engine No. 1 were extremely discouraging ... early in 1962 work was hastened, in parallel with detecting various problems on the test bench, to mount the engine on a test car so that its adaptability as an automotive engine could be tested. First of all, the prototype engine was installed in a small test car, but various problems were found when the car was put into operation. The engine ran very smoothly in high revolutions, but it became unsteady at slow speeds. When the engine brake was applied, strong vibrations occurred.

These problems—chatter marks, loss of output because of seal wear, "bucking" when the engine slowed down to idling speed— were common enough in early Wankel units. But the Matsudas' response was unusual in a company which was not a giant by anyone's standards. In 1960, it had a turnover of only $125 million, producing vehicles so small that their average selling price was $800. Yet they did not abandon the Wankel. In the engaging words of Kenichi Yamamoto: "We knew we needed the new engine to catch the leading companies. Our top management courageously adopted a tenacious mentality, and the whole company concentrated on this goal."

Fortunately, times were good for Toyo Kogyo's cars and trucks, as they had been for NSU's motorcycles when it had started to invest in rotary engine technology ten years before.

But the Wankel's problems were more severe than expected by either firm, and the boom in their orthodox businesses did not last long enough to support either company in its efforts to use the Wankel to jump into the big league of the motor industry. Toyo Kogyo now admits that the original decision was a gamble, but claims that it had been a necessary one if the company were to expand and keep its independence. It adds that "thanks to the Wankel, Toyo Kogyo's name is becoming well known."

Undeterred by the difficulties detected in these NSU engines, in April 1963 the Matsudas created a separate Rotary Engine Development Division. To head the division they chose a forty-year-old engineer, Kenichi Yamamoto, who in the succeeding few years emerged as one of the handful of men—Froede, Bentele, Bensinger of Daimler-Benz—who have made major contributions to rotary technology.

Yamamoto, locally born but educated at the elite Tokyo University, had started work after the war at the only job he could find, as an assembly line worker in the three-wheel Truck Division of Toyo Kogyo. He soon was transferred to the Engine Design Department, where he worked until the company's purchase of a license in 1961.

Yamamoto and a small team started work in an old, gloomy building with only five test benches to work on. But within nine months, the heart of a proper research operation—the test-cells in which engines could be run twenty-four hours a day—was ready, and by the autumn of 1964, a massive test block, with the operations fully computerized where necessary, had been completed.

This impressive physical apparatus was matched by the work done by Yamamoto and his engineers.*

By the time the new block was built, the Matsudas and Yamamoto had very clear ideas of the basic outline of the engine they wanted. To avoid low-speed problems, and hence the need for an automatic transmission, side ports had to be used. And to achieve the requisite blend of power and smoothness, two rotors rather than one were needed.

This still left two major intertwined practical problems—chatter marks and apex seals—and a host of smaller ones. For instance, the internal gears within the rotor tended to crack up. As the company puts it: "On the engines in the earlier stages, phenomena were sometimes seen as if the engines were having an epileptic fit, and when the engines were disassembled, it was found that the internal gears had broken to pieces."

Toyo Kogyo's engineers solved this problem by the straightforward, if technically complex, method of electrically measuring the forces acting on the gears' teeth and altering the design accordingly to cope with the stresses involved.

But the big problem was chatter marks. Says the company:

---

* Yamamoto's book on the Wankel is a standard textbook for engineering students on the construction of the engine. Wankel's own book was concerned with rotary engines in general. Yamamoto analyzes one by one all the problems faced by the Wankel configuration—the product of the work he and his colleagues did in the early and mid-1960s.

This was an extremely difficult problem which could not be overcome by merely working on ordinary seal materials or treating the trochoid surface in the ordinary way. It was necessary to test and try out every possible material available on this earth. Day in and day out, tests on the chatter marks were continued on the benches. Heaps of rotor housings, all with chatter marks, were soon piled high in the laboratory.

Within six months the engineers had devised an elaborate method of drilling two intersecting holes in the metal seal, resulting in a design called the "cross-hollow" seal. What is more, Yamamoto proved to NSU, when he visited Germany in 1964, that this system would work. He and his research team then went on to devise a more practical solution.

Toyo Kogyo did not try to invent any new technology; they merely pursued research on existing lines more thoroughly than anyone else had done. ("Teutonic" thoroughness would seem an applicable description, if one were not comparing the Japanese with the Germans themselves.)

In conjunction with a Japanese carbon company, Toyo Kogyo developed a series of carbon compounds that had embedded specks of metal. Aluminum finally became the first choice. The aluminum strengthened the seals, while the soft carbon kept its self-lubricating and gradual wearing qualities. Again, the lavishness of the Matsudas' technical equipment helped; with seals as with gears, one key to Toyo Kogyo's success has been the thoroughness and sophistication of the company's inspection processes, in both cases involving "nondestructive testing," where advanced electronic techniques are used to test processes and components without destroying them in the process.

It first returned to the three-part seals devised by Jones and Bentele in an effort to reduce leakage; then after a period of rapid change in the early 1970s, during which time, according to an American engineer, "no two Mazda engines we stripped down looked alike," Toyo Kogyo concluded, in 1973, that relatively inflexible cast iron seals were best after all. They could be made only half as thick as carbon ones—three millimeters as against six millimeters—and they leaked less gas back into the intake chamber. Their exactness of fit began to matter enormously when the American pollution requirements on production engines came into force.

The previous notion of a short and flexible seal to cope with the slightly different sizes on the hot and cold sides of the rotor housing was simply not precise enough.

In contrast to NSU, Toyo Kogyo wanted to make sure that any rotary-engined vehicle it put on the market was properly tested. By anyone else's standards, Yamamoto and his team worked fast as well as thoroughly. But even they suffered periods of depression. Mainly, Yamamoto recalls, because of "the skepticism and criticism from the outside directed at our company's management. People wondered why we were wasting our time trying to develop this new engine. We couldn't even prove there was a commercial need for the engine even if we were successful in developing it."

The basic design of Toyo Kogyo's first rotary-engined car had been settled as early as 1963, which is why, when it finally appeared in 1967 as the Cosmo Sport, the bodywork looked somewhat awkward and dated. Throughout their history, Toyo Kogyo's rotary engines have been housed in uninspiring bodywork, but there has not been any hesitation in changing and updating the engines themselves. For instance, Yamamoto made a lot of changes in the porting arrangements, both before the first rotary-engined Mazda, the Cosmo 110S, was unveiled at the 1966 Tokyo Motor Show and while it was in limited production.

One prototype was built with purely peripheral ports; then another was made with purely side ports, but this reduced the performance too far to be suitable for the sports car in which it was originally installed. A bigger version, with twin side intake ports, was installed in the first batch of eighty Cosmos. These were tested in the extreme cold of the 1965–66 winter in Hokkaido, Japan's northernmost island, and some were loaned out to suppliers, dealers, and to self-drive hire car firms whose clients enjoyed abusing the engine's speed. Following the tests (which added up to 400,000 miles of test driving), Yamamoto reverted to a combination of side ports (which were used at low speeds) and peripheral ones which came into use only at higher revolutions, the sort of combi-port now favored by Outboard Marine Corporation on its rotary-engined snowmobiles. But he finally changed back to dual side ports for the engines for ordinary sedans.

These first models, the 110S, renamed the Cosmo Sport, and then called the R 130 when its power was increased from 110 to 130 bhp in 1969, were never meant for mass production. They were, after all, sports cars, the market for which in Japan is extremely limited; in fact, Toyo Kogyo produced only 232 rotary cars in 1967 and 5,261 in 1968. Yet in many respects they were similar to the engines that Toyo Kogyo was to mass-produce within a couple of years. All had twin rotors with carbon seals running on a chrome-lined aluminum trochoid housing; all had cast iron side housings and rotors. (At one point, Yamamoto whetted the appetite of speed fans by reporting that he had tested light-alloy rotors at speeds of up to 14,000 rpm.)

Yamamoto's thoroughness demanded not only changes in ports. He also took great pains with the cooling system; the preheating of the incoming gases to help with cold starts; the ignition system, where Toyo Kogyo has always provided two spark plugs per rotor; and above all, the sealing system. The side seals were of Toyo Kogyo's own design and so, of course, were the metallized carbon apex seals.

Nothing about the engine was cheap to make, including non-rotary items like the highly sophisticated four-barrel carburetors required to feed the dual intake ports. It is doubtful if Toyo Kogyo could have made the engines at all if it had not had its own Machine Tool Division to devise the necessary machinery. Certainly the company has rarely allowed any visitors into certain key areas of the plant, notably those where the engines were assembled—which, in early 1969 when the author visited the rotary factory, were totally unautomated. Neither the author nor most other visitors have been allowed into that section of the factory where the interior of the trochoid housings was ground into shape.

The reason given out by Toyo Kogyo for this secrecy is that it does not want outsiders to see processes that are a trade secret shared only by NSU and Toyo Kogyo. But NSU's own engineers have found it very difficult to see some of these processes. The real reason for this rotary bamboo curtain is probably only partly a desire to protect trade secrets—even from NSU—and partly a refusal to admit to the outside world just how much of the work on the rotary engine is still done either by hand or, as in the case of grinding the trochoid housings, by slow and uneconomical machinery.

The excessive cost of producing the engine was only one of Toyo Kogyo's problems. By the end of the 1960s, its financial position was by no means healthy. It had reached its peak of profitability in 1966, reaching nearly eight percent on sales, but then declined to around 4.1 percent on sales in 1970 and is still going down. In the five-year period of 1965–70, sales rose only by two-fifths to $477 million, virtual stagnation by Japanese standards.

Part of the problem had been the sheer cost of developing the rotary engine. Although the license itself had cost under $5 million, Toyo Kogyo spent over $50 million during the 1960s. Matsuda's firm adherence to smaller, basic vehicles also cost his company dear in the Japanese market, which was steadily growing more affluent in the 1960s. And its sales outlets within Japan were less well organized than those of its bigger competitors, particularly those of Toyota, possibly the most ruthlessly efficient motor company in the world. Toyo Kogyo was still relying heavily on the small trucks which had always been its mainstay until sales collapsed as Japan's millions of shopkeepers and farmers found they could afford a proper car. And abroad Toyo Kogyo made little more than a token effort to increase its sales during a decade when Nissan, and Toyota, after mopping up most of the Southeast Asia market, sent their cars throughout the world, even invading the United States very successfully.

In contrast, Toyo Kogyo exported only 11,000 vehicles in 1965. Five years later its exports, though up to 87,000, still represented only a fifth of production.

So Toyo Kogyo could not afford the luxury of a completely new car in which to display the virtues of its rotary units, as NSU had done in the RO80. Any car they made had to be able to take either a rotary or an orthodox reciprocating unit. Indeed, the first ordinary sedan in which Mazda put a rotary unit was the Familia sedan, a modest-sized family car, normally fitted with a 1,000- or 1,200-cc unit, and already a little past its prime, since it had been on the market since 1966, three years before it was Wankelized into the R-100 coupe. As even Jan Norbye, a most charitable observer, put it:

> The R-100 was obviously not put into production for a long-term run. It must be regarded as an interim model, representing a hybrid solution relying partly on obsolete chassis engineering and partly on innovative and thoroughly refined power unit design.

This "interim, hybrid" model had its virtues. To show off the engine's endurance and sporty potential, two R-100s were entered in the twenty-four-hour endurance race at the Spa circuit at Francor-champs in Belgium in early 1970, finishing respectably enough in fifth and sixth places. The company got its comeuppance in the same race the next year. Toyo Kogyo was so confident that it invited forty journalists and photographers to watch a rotary triumph. But after fifteen hours of driving, the car broke down.

All this while Toyo Kogyo was probing, in a desultory way, into a number of rather arbitrarily chosen export markets. Its rotary-engined cars helped it to become the sixth biggest selling imported car in Canada in the years up to 1970. This experience also provided Mazda with some real cold-weather experience that led to the addition of a device to inject a couple of drops of alcohol into the rotary before starting in subzero conditions. In 1971, the RX-2 replaced the R-100, though it was still a "hybrid" that had to be capable of using an orthodox engine as well.

In 1970, it was widely assumed that Toyo Kogyo would be forced to merge with Toyota sooner rather than later. The Japanese government had a "game-plan" to form all Japan's dozen or more motor companies into two groups led by Nissan and Toyota, respectively, at least in part to avoid the invasion of American capital the Japanese knew was coming. Also in 1970, Nissan took out a license to make Wankel engines and immediately started work on a scale and thoroughness sufficient to ensure that Toyo Kogyo monopoly of the rotary engine would be soon broken, and by a company with the resources to produce a truly new car that could take the fullest advantage of the rotary's qualities.

When Toyo Kogyo started to ship its R-100 cars to the United States in the middle of 1970, it looked like a last desperate effort to retain its independence. Instead, these few shiploads formed the advance guard for a fashion that was to have a profound effect—on the United States more than on Japan itself.

13

Rolls-Royce and the Rotary Diesel

The Wankel's advantages over the small, efficient, rapidly improving engines used in European motorcars were relatively marginal. But from the start, it did offer an exciting way of using another type of combustion altogether—the diesel, in which a cylinderful of air is compressed, a heavy oil is injected, and the mixture ignites without the need for any form of spark. In theory the rotary idea should have eliminated the diesel's usual disadvantages while retaining all its advantages.

The diesel starts with two major advantages over the spark-ignited engine: It uses considerably less fuel to provide a similar amount of power, and the life of the motor is considerably longer. But because the air must be compressed much more than in an engine ignited by a spark, every component has to be heavier. A diesel weighs up to three times as much as an equivalent orthodox engine.

It follows that diesels are more expensive to produce, partly because they are heavier, but also because they use, instead of simple carburetors, complex and precisely engineered fuel-injection pumps to provide an exactly timed and measured flow of fuel into the cylinders. Diesel combustion is also inherently noisier than spark ignition, producing a characteristic thump and creating a good deal of vibration that is particularly noticeable when the motor is idling.

A rotary diesel, on the other hand, would reduce the weight of the engine, its noise, and vibration, without entirely sacrificing its advantages in terms of fuel consumption. Because diesels have never been made in such large production runs as motorcar engines, the technical inertia produced by enormous investments in existing production facilities was less important. Also, the cost of an individual unit did not have the same overriding importance as with gasoline engines. Producing a new—and more expensive—type of unit would seem a more acceptable type of risk if it were intended for the diesel market.

There was also a very personal factor involved. Felix Wankel had always seen himself as the third in a Holy Trinity of German engineers who had invented modern motoring. A century ago Nikolaus Otto had perfected the four-stroke cycle named after him, a cycle to which even Wankel's engine conformed. A few years later, Rudolf Diesel had demonstrated that if you compressed air sufficiently and injected oil at the right moment, it would ignite without the need for a spark of any sort. Then came Wankel with the rotary engine. A rotary diesel engine, combining these three ideas, seems a logical development. There should have been a whole rash of Wankel diesels. Instead, there has so far been only one working machine, which was made on an experimental basis by a British manufacturer of jet engines for the British Army.

As always in the Wankel story, the reasons behind this curious state of affairs are partly technical. The problems involved in bringing together rotary motion and diesel ignition have been considerable. Another factor has been the compartmentalized thinking of modern industry, which has hampered the expansion of the diesel's market. In trucks, it has an almost complete monopoly of everything above the size of a delivery van and a fair share of that market as well. It is increasingly used in taxis (made by Daimler, Peugeot and, GM's Opel subsidiary), where the fuel forms such an important element in the cost of running the vehicle. But its weight, its cost, its complexity and precision of manufacture, its characteristic thump —all these disadvantages have kept it from widespread use in cars. It appears to make little difference that it would last twice as long and use only two-thirds as much fuel as an orthodox engine; the customers, and thus the manufacturers, have not been very enthusiastic.

In the United States, vehicle users are less concerned about fuel economy than Europeans, for fuel has historically cost far less there than in Europe. The diesel, as a consequence, does not even enjoy a monopoly of the heavy truck market.

But even in the eyes of European vehicle manufacturers, the

rotary diesel was never regarded as a means of extending the diesel market, but as a direct competitor for the large and economical units used in trucks. The rotary's major advantages, its lightness and smoothness, were not considered crucially important factors when comparing engines for heavy trucks, and the additional cost of buying a reciprocating diesel can be quickly amortized over mileages of 50,000 a year or more.

One of the first companies to take an active interest in the Wankel was one of the world's biggest specialized diesel engine manufacturers, Perkins of Peterborough, in Britain. At the end of the 1950s, Perkins's position as an independent engine supplier was threatened by some of its major customers' starting to build their own engines. Monty Prichard, Perkins's amiable, rumple-faced managing director, who looks like Spencer Tracy, was persuaded by his friend Max Bunford to investigate the Wankel for possible use either as a diesel or in the outboard motor business Perkins had recently bought for diversification. Perkins worked on the engine for a couple of years and, in August 1961, took out the first license granted covering diesel applications. But the efforts came to nothing: In 1957 Perkins had been taken over by the Canadian Massey-Ferguson group, which sold the outboard business that was the major reason for taking out a license in the first place. Perkins was further put off the Wankel when it realized it could not sell loose engines directly to its many customers in the United States because of the terms of Curtiss-Wright's license. In fact, following several more years of desultory research, in 1965 Perkins actually gave up its license—the first and, so far, the only company to do so (though several have only taken options which they allowed to run out).

Perkins's interest had, however, served one of Bunford's purposes. It spurred the German diesel manufacturers into action. Clearly, they could not let a non-German company pioneer so Teutonic an idea as a diesel Wankel. So, shortly after Perkins had taken out its license, in 1961, a group of the major German truck manufacturers—MAN, Krupp, Klockner-Humboldt-Deutz, and, later, Daimler-Benz—all took out licenses and formed themselves into a formidable "Wankel Diesel Club." But this Wankel club was a committee, which inevitably lacked the imagination to overcome the major technical problem involved in trying to turn the rotary diesel idea into practice.

The required degree of compression to make a mixture of oil and air ignite without a spark is expressed as a "compression ratio," which measures how many times the air is compressed between the point in the cycle when the space in cylinder is at its biggest and when it is at its smallest. With a spark engine, this is between 7.5 and 10 to 1, as it is with a gasoline Wankel. With a diesel the figure is doubled—between 16 and 18 for larger diesels, possibly 20 or more to 1 for the small, fast diesels used in automobiles like GM's Opel.

Increasing the compression in a reciprocating diesel engine is not inordinately difficult. Less space is allowed in the combustion chamber above the piston when it is at the top of its stroke; in order to cope with the additional strains involved in compressing the air to a greater degree, the cylinder block, crankshaft, connecting rods, and pistons are made heavier than with a spark engine—the major reason for the diesel's weight penalty. But the whole shape of a Wankel's combustion chamber changes as the compression ratio is increased, giving a flatter and thus more elongated space at the point of ignition.

This alters the situation greatly to the Wankel's disadvantage, for the perfect shape to burn gases efficiently is as compact and nearly spherical as possible. Yet, as the compression ratio on a Wankel mounts, the combustion chamber gets steadily flatter and more banana-shaped, and hence much less efficient in burning fuel. Technically, the efficiency is judged by the "surface-to-volume ratio," for clearly a thin, flat, banana-shaped chamber contains less air or gas for a given area of wrapping than does a compact and spherical one (a rounded chamber is inevitably more efficient as a container). In the elongated shape, arrived at when increasing the compression ratio on a Wankel, the surfaces are relatively so big that they remain cold; the fuel clings to them and does not burn; and the flame, once generated, has a long way to travel. In contrast, in an efficient reciprocating diesel unit, a great deal of mixture is contained in a chamber which, if not purely circular, approximates a slightly squashed orange. This accentuates the "swirling" of the mixture, stirring fuel and air like a martini, whereas in the rotary the mixture remains separate, like a mayonnaise gone wrong. There seemed no way of improving the compression to reduce the Wankel's disadvantage.

Wankel himself had foreseen the problem and warned the licensees that it was futile to simply try to turn an ordinary rotary into a diesel. Yet the Wankel Diesel Club persisted for four years in their experiments and spent over $10 million. They not only found that combustion was inefficient, but also that the strains on the materials used were such that over twenty experimental engines cracked up under test. Not a single one showed any real promise of being durable enough. The problem required a more radical solution. So far two have been proposed, one from Wankel himself, the other from a more unexpected direction—the great British engine firm of Rolls-Royce.

Rolls-Royce is best known for its motorcars, though since the war it has depended for the bulk of its business on jet engines. Almost as a sideline, it manufactures diesel engines for heavy trucks. But in the fifties and sixties, it was dominated by self-confident engineers, enthusiasts for new ideas, sure that they could make them work and able to convince their customers of that fact—in particular the British armed forces.

The tone of Rolls-Royce was set by its then chief executive, Sir Denning Pearson, himself a brilliant aeroengineer.

Rolls-Royce—or rather, Dr. Rubbra, its inquisitive roving technical adviser—spotted the Wankel and tested one. Pearson saw it on the test bed and was equally excited by it. More to the point, a young engineer, Fritz Feller, from the small division that made the reciprocating engines for the Rolls-Royce cars, as well as its diesel engines, fell in love with the Wankel.

Feller, born in Austria but educated in Britain, spotted a use for the Wankel. At the time, in the early 1960s, he was working on studies for the British Army to find an engine suitable for new armored vehicles. At the time, "multifuel capability"—the ability of an engine to be flexible enough to use any type of oil-based liquid as fuel—was the military fashion, particularly at the Pentagon. But if there is no regular diesel fuel or one of the many heavy oils suitable for diesels in a battle area, it is a fair bet there will not be any other oily liquid around either.

Rolls-Royce's work on a multifuel engine provided Feller with an excellent opportunity to persuade the British Army to take up any new ideas he might have. He saw that a rotary diesel was a potentially suitable motor for a tank, especially one that could be transported by air. In a study for the British Army's Fighting Vehicles Research Establishment, Feller demonstrated—in theory—how much lighter and more compact a rotary would be compared with any reciprocating engine. In the case of a tank, the Wankel's disadvantages—its cost, its possible lack of durability, and its thirst for fuel—were not important.

Like Bentele at Curtiss-Wright, and Yamamoto at Toyo Kogyo, but unlike most of the other engineers involved in the Wankel, Feller had the time to study the engine's basic problems. He quickly grasped that the compression required for a rotary diesel could not be achieved in a simple engine. The air going into the combustion chamber would have to be compressed to some extent beforehand, so that the compression achieved by the combustion rotor itself did not have to be too high. As the Germans had already discovered to their bitter cost, it was impossible to compress the air too much in a simple chamber and still provide a container in which efficient combustion was possible.

Feller saw that there were three alternative ways to compress the air before it was fed to the rotor chamber in which combustion would take place. The first was a Roots blower (a pair of interlocking peanut-shaped paddles which rotate together and compress the air); the second, a turbocharger using the energy from the exhaust gases to compress the incoming air; and, finally, the addition of another cylinder or rotor to each combustion unit. The first two solutions were rejected early on; the Roots blower used too much power, and the turbocharger created problems when the engine was first started and there were no hot exhaust gases to use. Feller also wanted to retain the advantages of sticking purely to the rotary principle and therefore rejected the idea that the secondary booster should be reciprocating, or should include valves. He tried a number of combinations and shapes for the combustion chamber within the rotor (his office is littered with wooden models of rejected designs). In addition, he tried thirty different designs of rotor depressions, not to mention six different positions for the fuel injector.

Using a modified NSU test engine, in two years he had proved the crucial point: Given a supply of precompressed air, a rotary diesel would give fuel consumption substantially better than that of a spark-fired gasoline-fueled reciprocating unit (though still worse than a really efficient reciprocating diesel unit).

He had also started work on two separate multirotor designs for precompressing the air, first by using a three-rotor system, and, more promisingly, by using two rotors. The larger one provided the first stage of compression and fed the compressed air to the smaller high-pressure unit, where the fuel was injected and the mixture ignited. The combustion gases produced some power during their expansion phase in the smaller chamber, before passing back through the bigger chamber to provide more power. The cumulative effect was like the double expansion of a locomotive's steam engines or the compounding of Wright's last successful aeroengine.

The idea worked well enough for the three-rotor idea to be dropped; though once Feller had proved his theoretical points, he then came up against the familiar Wankel problems of stress—especially on the apex seals.

To produce the engine, Rolls-Royce needed a license; it would have liked to work with the German members of the Diesel Club. But, as with Perkins, the Germans' pride was affronted at the idea that a non-German company could have anything to contribute to the rotary diesel. They refused to countenance Roll's suggestion of a pact to pool information and technical ideas. (Rolls naturally refused their requests to be allowed access to its work years later, when the tables were turned.)

Even getting a license was not that easy. By the time Rolls-Royce came on the scene, Henn and Hutzenlaub had laid down their guidelines and were trying to sell only specialized licenses. Rolls-Royce, producing only forty cars a week, could not afford a license for a gasoline rotary and, in any case, never innovated very much in the technical specifications of its cars. But even to get the limited license, it needed to produce larger diesels, and multifuel engines (from 100 to 850 bhp) meant a clash of cultures between the gentlemanly negotiating habits of Rolls-Royce and the somewhat tougher methods practiced by Henn and Hutzenlaub. At one point, indeed, the two German negotiators serverely embarrassed their putative English partners by shouting—at each other—at some length in the genteel calm of a British country hotel.

Finally, early in 1965, a deal was made, and Rolls-Royce became a member of the Wankel Club. As Feller proved, with successively larger engines, that his principles would produce the necessary power, he became one of the handful of rotary engineers respected throughout the world. Even Wankel himself, never the first to acknowledge other people's work, has a painting by Feller (naturally of a rotary engine) in his study.

Although Feller had made the necessary breakthrough, Rolls-

Royce was not the right company to produce the rotary diesel. For the reciprocating diesel engine presented too fast a moving a target. By the early 1970s, Rolls-Royce could put on its test beds ordinary diesel engines for use in heavy trucks whose fuel consumption and durability were so good that the Wankel could not compete as a power unit in the foreseeable future. And Rolls had no use for a smaller unit.

By that time, too, Pearson had departed in disgrace from his bankrupt group.* The division for which Feller worked had been reorganized as a separate, independent company, finding its own way in the world and in no position to develop the unit further itself. Feller himself had moved on to dreaming up even more advanced, glamorous, and hopefully profitable designs of motorcars. Although Feller had successfully proved his thesis that for the early development of a a new idea, a small, flexible group can achieve more than a massive crash program, he and his team had got as far as they could. To turn what was still an experimental engine into a production unit required considerably more funds.

In October 1973, the Yom Kippur War destroyed the long-term reasoning behind the engine's development for use in tanks. New, portable antitank missiles had tipped the balance against armor. The development of a new air-borne tank lost its place in the army's procurement program. Cancelation of the program was inevitable, and it came in May 1974.

Feller's was not the only solution to the problems posed by the rotary diesel. Yanmar Diesel, the Japanese company, had patented ideas for a double chamber somewhat similar to his, though, judging by its total silence on the subject, it has not made much practical progress. But Wankel himself, working for the Wankel Diesel Club which had earlier rejected his advice, came up with an even more radical solution, though one based on Feller's principle that some form of precompression was necessary.

During his lifelong study of rotary shapes, Wankel had cataloged hundreds of different combinations of rotors and chambers and therefore did not feel restricted to the three-sided rotor which bears

---

* Pearson's disregard for mere financial considerations eventually led to his downfall and his firm's bankruptcy and nationalization. He hopelessly underestimated the cost and complexity of developing the RB 211 engines used in the Lockheed Tri-Star.

his name. Like Feller, he proposed a double chamber, but one in which neither of the rotors would be triangular. The booster rotor would be a simple paddle-shaped two-sided affair, rotating in a circular chamber. And the combustion rotor would be four-sided, revolving in a three-compartment chamber. This would give a five-stage combustion cycle, instead of the four-stage cycle usual in reciprocating or other rotary engines, with two combustion-expansion stages. By 1972, Wankel had overcome the practical difficulties involved (including the need for a very special high-speed fuel injector) and actually had one working in his institute at Lindau.

As is so often the case in the Wankel story, business politics are preventing any speedy development of either Feller's or Wankel's ideas. Any further work would have to be funded by Wankel International, now controlled by Lonrho, and Lonrho—or rather, Tiny Rowland—resolutely refuses to invest in any serious research. He got as far as agreeing on a program with the world's leading researchers into the problems of diesel combustion—the firm of Ricardo, located, improbably enough, in the small English seaside town of Shoreham. But the money to turn the ideas into test beds has never been forthcoming.

The best practical hope for the rotary diesel lies not in Germany, which invented the principles, nor in England, which made them work, but in the United States. General Motors, as part of its massive rotary program, has been working for a couple of years now on a rotary diesel and has studied Feller's ideas very carefully. GM's Detroit Diesel Division, the largest maker of reciprocating diesels in the United States, is handling the rotary diesel program and it certainly has the technical know-how. It may also have the vision to see that the rotary diesel is primarily suitable for cars, where the competition is the thirstier petrol engine and where bulk and weight are vitally important.

There could be no better demonstration that a rotary need not be an uneconomical engine than for GM, in these times of expensive fuel, to produce a rotary diesel for cars that could use a third less fuel than an orthodox petrol-driven competitor. Feller has proved such an engine is possible, and it only remains for someone else to scale down his rotary diesel, designed to move the massive weight of a tank, for use in a passenger automobile.

14

Nonautomotive Uses

As early as 1960, Dr. Froede of NSU had foreseen that the first applications of the Wankel principle would be in a stationary engine running at a constant speed and load, like those used in generators and pumps. He thought this would be followed by its installation in light aircraft and boats, where there is a specific load corresponding to each engine speed. In all these uses, the Wankel could be operated at its high potential working speeds, thus ensuring that a minimal size of unit would be used for any given power and, because the engines in aircraft and boats operate at relatively constant speeds, the strains placed on the various seals would be minimized.

Dr. Froede could have logically made a further point: The non-motoring users of power had already taken up two other alternative engines to the four-stroke reciprocating gasoline engine, the jet (or gas turbine) and the two-stroke reciprocating engine, in which every downward movement of the piston produces power. But, as with the rotary diesel, any accelerated development program for a rotary engine for nonmotor purposes required a sponsor—preferably the free-spending military, who by expensive crash programs had compressed the development of the jet engine from decades into a few years. In the absence of such wholehearted commitment on the part of the military, progress was bound to be slower. In this field, none of the companies involved had resources comparable to the motor companies to hurry the research along.

Despite the Rolls-Royce diesel contract with the British Army, the Wankel was never likely to get the sort of massive defense support given to the jet. Its advantages over reciprocating engines were not overwhelming enough for any specific purpose to make it a military priority item.

148

The Wankel suffered the additional disadvantage in its non-automotive development that, apart from Rolls-Royce, it had not been taken up by any of the world's defense departments' favorite suppliers. The logical backer was Curtiss-Wright, holder of the major license outside the auto industry. But its management actually hindered the spread of the engine, not just for any conceivable military purposes, but for all nonautomobile uses as well. As we have seen, Hurley ruined the firm's previously cozy relationship with the U.S. Defense Department in the fifties, and his successors were not dynamic enough to force the Pentagon to take any notice of them. Even more important, the Curtiss-Wright management never provided the world with a rotary power plant or a rotary vehicle to show off its capabilities. Hurley's notion of putting an engine into a luxury private motorboat was perfectly sensible and would almost certainly have provided the engine with the flagship which it lacked throughout the 1960s and which the RO80 so sadly failed to provide. This crippling lack of imagination has ensured that the engine's impact on the nonautomotive field, military and nonmilitary, has been more belated and fragmentary than it would otherwise have been.

But Curtiss-Wright's coupon-clipping standpattism since Hurley's departure is in startling contrast with the attitude of Savkel—the only other Wankel licensee that did not already produce other kinds of competing engines or vehicles that might be modified to take a rotary. Every other licensee had made its investment defensively, as a protection measure. Only Hurley and the men at the Israeli-British Bank (IBB) behind Savkel had no immediate use for the engine. Savkel of Hadera is owned partly by the Israeli-British Bank, partly by American-Israeli Paper Mills, an Israeli company quoted on the American Stock Exchange, and partly by a private company owned by William J. Levitt, the man who invented Levittowns.

Savkel is a deliberate act of imagination, but then, says a Savkelman, "The whole state of Israel was an act of the imagination."

The IBB had been interested in the potential of the Wankel since the mid-1960s and, as seen in Chapter 10, was deeply involved in the takeover of NSU by Volkswagen. Part of the settlement following the bank's involvement was Savkel's unusually broad license agreement, expanded in 1972, after a further agreement with Curtiss-Wright. Savkel is allowed to produce gasoline engines from one-half to 150 horsepower (bhp) for industrial uses, with options to produce engines for use in land vehicles and in aircraft.

The reasoning behind the Savkel development is that Israel, a country with few immediately available raw materials but a mass of skilled manpower, is better able to develop new projects, like the Wankel, which use advanced production techniques. Hence the license, hence the enthusiastic backing of the Israeli government, hence the purchase of the stake in Savkel in 1973 by Levitt, an enthusiastic Zionist whose yacht is often moored in Haifa harbor.

Savkel's aim is clear: to develop a range of rotary engines, using Curtiss-Wright's expertise and to be built in Israel, primarily for export, mainly to the United States. As usual, the plans—designed to produce 100,000 engines a year—have been delayed, at least in one case, for an unusual reason: Virtually the entire Savkel engineering staff had to go to the front during the 1973 war, leaving only a handful of women engineers and Curtiss-Wright advisers at work. Savkel's ideas are broad; for example, it has tested one engine for 1,000 hours as a portable generator. It has plans to market others in the United States through Curtiss-Wright for use in golf carts and other "leisure" vehicles.

But, as is so often the case in Israel, there is also a military rationale. The Israeli Army is still seriously interested in developing a Wankel for use in tanks—an interest apparently undimmed by the lessons of the October War which led Rolls-Royce and the British Army to abandon their rotary program.

If the Israelis do find a genuine military use for the motor, they will be setting a precedent. The Rolls-Royce contract proved to be technically important, but, in military terms, was always of peripheral interest.

Despite the damage Hurley had done to Curtiss-Wright's reputation with the Pentagon, the engine did find its way into a few experimental military playthings during the 1960s. Variants of its sturdy RC 2-60 unit were installed in an armored personnel carrier, a Ferret scout car, and in a Reo 2½-ton six-wheel drive truck. Another use of the engine was in a Wankel-powered electrical generator (developed by Curtiss-Wright in conjunction with Westinghouse) that could be transported by air to meet the needs of forward combat systems like radar stations or mobile missile launchers. But the engine was only marginally lighter than one of its rivals—the gas turbine—and only fifteen percent less bulky.

In an airplane, the Wankel's quietness, lack of vibration, and small size should be significant. One problem was that the gas turbine—and the hybrid turboshaft, where a jet engine drives a propeller—had got there first. Besides, the market for either reciprocating or rotary units was limited. Fewer than 30,000 nonjet aircraft engines are sold each year in the United States.

Nevertheless, Hurley seized the opportunity and by 1960 had designed and built the world's first multibank rotary, with four rotors developing 425 hp. Hurley claimed that this engine would be especially suitable for hot climates, because the rotary did not require components like exhaust valves which often caused trouble in reciprocating engines. But Hurley's successors canceled the program, and during the 1960s Curtiss-Wright was forced to rely on the vagaries of the U.S. military to get a rotary actually airborne.

The first aircraft powered by a Wankel engine used another version of the reliable old RC 2-60. It was installed in a Lockheed-built reconnaissance plane called the Q-Star, based on a two-passenger glider. And it looked very curious too. The engine was mounted behind the pilot and connected to a propeller mounted in the front and above his head by a long shaft. It was tested in Vietnam in 1968. According to Karl Ludvigsen, the troops "took the sound of its six-bladed prop for the fluttering wings of a flock of birds," a report which must, surely, come into *The New Yorker's* category of "mistakes we doubt ever got mistook." (The Luftwaffe had been the first to try a Wankel in an aircraft. It was installed in a glider as a possible light aircraft trainer. The plane had two specially developed thirty-horsepower engines with a "shrouded" propeller tucked away inside the fuselage, thus using one of the Wankel's most neglected advantages—its ability to deliver power reliably at very high speeds, much faster than more orthodox units. A shrouded propeller can be run at very high rpms directly from the engine without any need for the complicated gearing normally used to reduce the engine's speed to a level suitable for an orthodox propeller.)

But reciprocating aircraft engines are improving so fast that they present a difficult, moving target for a new engine. A three-sided battle has developed among the older piston engine, the Wankel, and a new generation of small, lightweight turboshafts. (Ironically, Max Bentele worked on turboshafts as a consultant for Avco-Lycoming, after he had left Curtiss-Wright.)

In this race (for only 30,000 units, most in private planes), the

Wankel looks like a loser, unless Curtiss-Wright, uncharacteristically, is brave enough (skeptics would say foolhardy) to actually put an engine into even limited production in advance of any absolute assurance that customers are available.

Prospects for the Wankel are, however, much more promising in helicopters, where its relative freedom from vibration and its lightness make it theoretically an ideal unit. In fact, in Hurley's days, Curtiss-Wright had designed an elaborate and ultralightweight unit, complete with fuel injection, for possible use in helicopters and unmanned target drones. But it was not until 1973 that a Wankel RC 2-60 was installed in a helicopter under a Pentagon contract to Hughes Aircraft for the development of a new training helicopter.

The rotary unit proved dramatically lighter and more compact than a reciprocating unit; the vibration level was reduced by half. On the other hand, the Wankel helicopter did not respond quickly enough to the throttle, a fault correctable by fuel injection. But this addition needed more time and money than was available.°

The world of radio-controlled model airplanes is still seemingly locked in the mortal combats of World War I, with miniature Red Barons everlastingly repeating their triumphs over the Sopwith Camels of their opponents. But the engine vibrations reduce the pleasure of the band of enthusiasts who continue to keep their legend alive. The models carry tiny radio receivers. If they use miniature reciprocating engines, these radio sets must be swaddled in thick layers of foam rubber to absorb the vibrations. With the Wankel the foam rubber is unnecessary. A unique example of German-Japanese cooperation had led to the rotary's most picturesque success story —and its smallest model, the size of a tangerine, with a weight of only twelve ounces.

Johannes Graupner, the well-known German manufacturer of model airplane kits, first became interested in the Wankel after the 1960 Munich symposium had exposed it for the first time to serious academic comment. Graupner, not itself an engine maker, subcon-

---

° The freedom from vibration is a much underrated virtue of the Wankel. In one area, it can give the engine an edge. Lumbermen, who regularly use chain saws powered by reciprocating engines, endemically get the disagreeable industrial disease called "white candle." Nerve ends in the fingers are shattered by the constant vibrations, and the fingers turn a waxy white. Rotary engines do not vibrate; hence there is a considerable interest among makers of chain saws, one of whom, the German Stihl company, actually makes a Wankel-powered chain saw.

tracted the work to Herr Schaegg of the Fraunhofer Engineering Foundation, which did a lot of work on the Wankel for Daimler-Benz. Schaegg could only work on the engine part time, but within three years he had designed a rotary which used the same fuel and the same type of ignition as existing model aircraft engines; like them, it was air-cooled, was the same size (around five cubic centimeters), and ran at the same speed, between 12,000 and 14,000 rpm. He went on improving the design and, by May 1967, Graupner was proudly flying a Wankel-powered aircraft at the model airplane's world championships. Only then did it take out a license— still the only one for engines as small as this.

Having successfully subcontracted the design work, Graupner then looked around for another company actually to manufacture the unit and found the Japanese Ogawa Seiki (OS), model aeroengine specialists as well as willing partners. It took OS another two years before they had an engine in production because there was no machinery available for grinding the inside of the trochoid housing —even for a Wankel of five cubic centimeters.

The first OS Wankel, like so many pioneering efforts in the rotary field, was not a success. Peter Chinn, one of the world's leading model engine experts, comments:

When we examined and tested our preproduction OS Wankel motor in 1969, we were impressed by the engineering that had been put into it and fascinated by the fact that it really worked, so much so that it just had to go into a model for the novelty of seeing it fly. . . . Viewed quite dispassionately, however, one could have said that it appeared to offer no advantages over a conventional model aircraft engine except smoother operation and a better shape. Compared with a good orthodox 0.30 cubic-inch engine, it was heavier, more difficult to start, offered no improvement powerwise, and lacked a really low idling speed. At this stage, therefore, the engine's critics could have said, with some justification, that it was a wonderful collector's item but stood little chance of competing with existing model two-cycle motors.

A proper Wankel engine, though it did without side seals and a separate lubrication system, this engine had problems in common with other early designs. Despite special cooling fins, the engine "ran extremely hot and lost power as it warmed up." But even the early version "produced only a fraction of the vibration" of an equivalent engine.

Within a couple of years, OS had succeeded in minimizing the disadvantages of the Wankel, although it still ran for only fifty hours, half the duration of its competing unit. However, the radio equipment lasted much longer because of the absence of vibrations. As usual, the apex seals (which were of cast iron) received the most attention—in the end they had to be fitted to an accuracy of 1/10,000 of an inch. The many other detailed changes produced an engine worth the extra price, with "high power, excellent throttling, easy handling, smooth running, quiet, easy to mount, compact." Even now OS is producing only a few thousand rotaries a year (though these are eagerly snapped up, especially in the United States), which is a fraction of its annual output of 150,000 units.

There is one type of power unit that looked—and still looks —immensely vulnerable to the challenge of the Wankel. This was the two-stroke reciprocating engine. Noisier, more polluting, and less efficient in its use of fuel than a four-stroke unit, or indeed a Wankel, it has the overwhelming advantage of simplicity. There are no valves or other apparatus that so complicates a reciprocating four-stroke engine.

Since the turn of the century, they have been produced by the millions and are, therefore, very cheap. These engines are often sold separately—as outboard motors, for instance—which means a competitor for their customers has an additional hurdle to overcome.

As Karl Ludvigsen notes:

It is a special challenge of this [outboard motor] market that the price is simply of the engine and not a car or a boat with an engine in it, in which the extra cost of a more expensive power unit could be hidden somewhere. Any additional cost in an outboard engine or an industrial engine is immediately visible in the market price of the product.

What were the Wankel's advantages for this market? They were certainly different from those it offered compared to a four-stroke engine. The Wankel promised to the customers for a two-stroke reciprocating engine less vibration and less polluting exhaust. Even the Wankel's fuel consumption was less than the two-stroke engine's.

On the other hand, the engine would cost more, however large the scale on which it was produced.

To develop a Wankel to compete with the two-stroke engine required a combination of circumstances. The developing firm had to be a major force in the market already, or it would not have either the resources or the distribution network required. It must be technically enterprising and not afraid of the long haul.

The Japanese company Yanmar Diesel was the first manufacturer to market a rotary outboard motor. Yanmar, like Toyo Kogyo, was very much the creation of one man.

Magokichi Yamoaka, who ran the company for fifty years after he founded it in 1912, was an austere old autocrat. The whole management, himself included, had to work together in one wooden shack with their desks all crammed together. Only after his death did his son and successor move the managers into more appropriate accommodations.

Yanmar's main business was in producing the diesel engines used by Japanese fishermen. Because it had no reputation to lose, it could afford to market a rotary outboard. But Yamoaka's rotary ambitions were extensive. The license he took out in July 1961 (the first in Japan, two days before Toyo Kogyo) covered all possible uses for the engine except in aircraft and automobiles for the whole world, apart from the United States.

Since 1961, Yanmar has been engaged on a silent, and apparently fruitless, effort to develop a rotary diesel for the market it knows best—Japanese fishing boats. It did succeed by 1970 in producing a couple of small outboard motors of twenty-eight and fifty-six horsepower. As with all rotary pioneers, Yanmar had problems with seals and cooling, but by 1972 a new generation of the engine was being sold in Japan and in Australia, where they have allegedly proved very popular. But these rotaries are very expensive, use more fuel than a comparable two-stroke engine, and are heavier and bulkier than competitive units, which makes it unsurprising that today Yanmar only makes a few thousand of them a year.

Although Briggs and Stratton, the world's biggest manufacturer of two-stroke engines, has been notably indifferent to the engine, two other companies in the market—Fichtel and Sachs in Germany and Outboard Marine in the United States—have emerged as perhaps the only companies in the Wankel story to have behaved in the sort of balanced yet enterprising fashion so beloved of management textbooks.

Fichtel and Sachs is one of the most important manufacturers of motor components in Germany. Its first success came at the turn of the century with the ball bearings that enabled bicycles to free-wheel. Today it is best known for its automatic transmissions made for Volkswagens and the RO80. (An even wider public has heard of Gunther Sachs, a member of the founding family, who was once married to Brigitte Bardot, and who is now an active vice-chairman of the company, stoutly maintaining that his playboy days are behind him.)

Fichtel and Sachs produce over 300,000 two-stroke engines a year. Since, like many other German companies at the time, its board of directors was very technically oriented, it was easily persuaded by its technical director, Dr. Josef von Bomhard, to take out a Wankel license as early as December 1960, after a year of testing air- and water-cooled rotary engines. Fichtel and Sachs marketed its first rotary engine, the KM37, producing three horsepower at 3,000 rpm and seven horsepower at 6,000 rpm, three and a half years later. Apart from the unit produced in very small numbers a couple of years before by NSU for use by water-skiers, the KM37 was the first Wankel engine marketed anywhere in the world.

Fichtel and Sachs's achievement was the more remarkable because it was tackling a whole range of new markets for the engine. The company did not get much help from NSU and Curtiss-Wright which, in the early 1960s, were the only sources of information on the engine.

The Fichtel and Sachs engineers were concerned above all with compactness and the cost of construction. They were aiming to build a robust and reliable unit for a large range of applications, from chain saws to lawn mowers. Because of the relatively small size of the unit, they could take a number of technical shortcuts—using cast iron rotors, a simple standard spark plug, and using air-cooling which had proved inadequate for larger engines. The rotor could be cooled by the gases entering the engine ("charge cooling") which, though reducing combustion efficiency and, again, would have been wildly unsuitable for auto uses, was not a handicap in this market. And because users of lawnmowers and chain saws are used to adding a small drop of oil to the fuel they use to make it suitable for the two-stroke engines normally fitted, Fichtel and Sachs could afford to ask users of their rotary to do the same.

Initially, the KM37 was not wholly successful. For one thing, Fichtel and Sachs made an engine suitable for a very wide variety of uses; so it was not especially well adapted for any one of them. In addition, like other early Wankel manufacturers, Fichtel and Sachs's engine suffered from the dreaded chatter marks and the wearing away of the apex seals. Fichtel and Sachs tried carbon, aluminum, Teflon, and chrome, among other materials, for the apex seals.

Nor was the engine that profitable. It cost more to make than had been expected—twice as much as a two-stroke engine of similar output. To justify that price, the Wankel unit had to be extremely reliable, but because of it Fichtel and Sachs produced only a few thousand a year, compared with its output of 300,000 to 400,000 of ordinary two-stroke engines, which, of course, lost the Wankel the cost reduction inherent to large-scale production. And sales were affected by the well-publicized bad reputation acquired by the rotaries used in the NSU Spyder and RO80 cars, even though Fichtel and Sachs's units proved reliable at the relatively low-stress uses they were designed for.

Nevertheless, Fichtel and Sachs persisted. When chrome was replaced by Elnisil as the lining for the trochoid housing, Fichtel and Sachs breathed a collective sigh of relief. In the words of one of its engineers, this change "provided the justification for producing the Sachs Wankel engine."

By the end of the 1960s, Fichtel and Sachs was producing a range of engines, up to twenty-three horsepower or more, suitable for the new and booming U.S. snowmobile market. Originally, Fichtel and Sachs was forced to sell its engines through Curtiss-Wright, but eventually renegotiated the contract to enable it to use another distributor. Fichtel and Sachs chose the Minnesota-based Arctic Enterprises, which sold 23,000 units within a few years, mainly for lawn mowers, largely on the engine's appeal as a novelty. By the early 1970s, Fichtel and Sachs was beginning to reap the reward of its long-term support of the rotary. It was one of the very few companies in a position to take advantage of the great Wankel boom in the United States that occurred at the start of the decade. In early 1973, when one of its distributors ran a single advertisement in the

Wall Street Journal offering three Fichtel and Sachs units ranging from eight to twenty-three horsepower, it was "overwhelmed" with inquiries from manufacturers of everything from irrigation pumps to small airplanes.

More important, Fichtel and Sachs was able to exploit the painfully learned experience of ten years with the KM37 and introduce a replacement, the KM3, which demonstrated dramatically the degree to which experience can lead to simpler, more specialized, and more profitable engines—and thus refute critics who judge the Wankel only from first-generation units. Because Fichtel and Sachs was so early on the Wankel scene, it was the first to show the benefit of development experience so soon and so clearly. The KM3 has about the same volume and produces slightly less power than the engine it replaces. The KM3's rotor is over two inches thick, nearly twice the width of the KM37's. Because the rotor itself is fatter, the volume is contained in a smaller package—since the radius of the rotor is so much smaller. Fichtel and Sachs intended the new engine for a specific use—in this case in lawn mowers—and therefore could design it for the most economical power output from a given size of unit, rather than the maximum at a higher speed.

The crucial difference is in the weight and simplicity of design. The KM37 weighed thirty-four pounds. The new engine weighs sixteen pounds, under half as much. The manufacturing costs are under a third of those for the old engine, which should put them marginally below those of a rival two-stroke unit. The cost reduction is partly due to the engine's reduced weight, which means less materials. Detailed attention to the whole design and one bold piece of simplification also contribute. The KM3 is designed to be installed directly above the blades of a lawn mower, with the lower side of the rotor resting on the housing. Fichtel and Sachs reasoned that they did not need an expensive side seal on the bottom of the rotor. They simply cut out a ridge on the rotor instead. The engine is air-cooled; so it needs cooling fins. But these are concentrated where they are really needed. There are none, for instance, on the cold intake side of the engine—giving the engine the appearance of a peacock's tail.

Fichtel and Sachs has not committed itself too heavily to the unit. On average, only about twenty-five engineers have been developing the engine at any one time. Yet it has managed to produce engines that have justified their high price by their novelty and reliability if not by really down-to-earth advantages. One mark of its success: Its output has proved inadequate for the distributors.

In the words of the technical director, von Bomhard, when he introduced the KM3:

We faced up to the question, "Could we make a successful breakthrough to a competitive product in this bracket of low output but high sales volume, or was the purchase of a Wankel license nothing more than an extravagant technical frivolity for our company?" I think we've made the breakthrough.

The breakthrough puts Fichtel and Sachs (and their Italian sub-licensees who supply a limited number of outboard engines to the United States) in a powerful position as independent suppliers of well-proven rotary engines for a wide variety of uses. The two best publicized so far have been in lawn mowers and snowmobiles, where the public fancy is capricious and fashion-conscious and rarely deterred by price. Even in less glamorous uses by price-conscious industrial customers, the Wankel's advantages should ensure some sort of future.

Outboard Marine Corporation (OMC), another nonautomotive specialist engine manufacturer, forms the other model case history of sensible Wankel development. OMC is best known to the public as the manufacturer of Johnson and Evinrude marine engines and snowmobiles. The outboard engine was, in fact, invented sixty years ago by one of its founders, delightfully named Ole Evinrude. OMC still makes more of them than anyone else.

While the motor manufacturers of the world were still looking askance at the Wankel engine, OMC was eagerly grasping its potential. In 1963, OMC's directors were shown two boats with different new power units, the first using jet propulsion on which a lot of development effort had been expended; then, almost as an afterthought, a boat powered by one of Curtiss-Wright's RC 2-60 engines. The directors immediately abandoned their jet efforts, and, encouraged by their research director, Jim Mohr, took out a preliminary Wankel license that same year and a full one (or rather two, one for the United States and one for worldwide development) three years later.

OMC's engineers faced a major challenge. Any new unit had to compete with the two-stroke engine, which was improving rapidly in power, reliability, and low cost. In 1973, for instance, the company's basic V-4 engine produced 135 bhp. In 1958, the bulkier equivalent could only manage 50 bhp. The two-stroke engine was also no longer as noisy. When OMC introduced a rotary-powered snowmobile in 1972, it did not emphasize quietness because there was a comparable reciprocating model that was four decibels quieter. In addition, any new engines had to aim for two distinct markets with different requirements. In the marine engine, a water-cooled unit was essential. In a snowmobile, the engine had to be air-cooled.

The choice of a snowmobile as the first test vehicle was partly because OMC already dominated the outboard market and a rotary would only have been taking away sales from its own reciprocating units.

OMC was a late comer to snowmobiles, a market which, by the end of the 1960s, had reached an amazing 500,000 units a year. Any rotary sales would come from the competition. On the other hand, the snowmobile provided the Wankel with a sterner test than an outboard, for which the speed is relatively stable and conditions do not vary very much. The snowmobile is used not only in winter snow, but also in summer on slippery summer grassland by pleasure seekers—or on the hot sands of Death Valley. The model therefore had to cope with temperatures ranging from below zero to over 100° Fahrenheit. As any snowmobile user will tell you, the rpms of the engine vary almost as much as with a motorcycle—from laboring up snow hills to coasting down the other side.

OMC also faced the problems of the pioneer. It held the first license in the United States after Curtiss-Wright and, in 1972, was the first manufacturer to produce a Wankel in North America. No one was interested in providing the specialized machine tools to do the crucial work of machining the inside of the housing, and OMC had to do its own design work. Luckily, its self-taught manufacturing manager, Eugene Kraeger, stayed on years after his scheduled retirement date to nurse the engine through its production teething troubles.

OMC, like Fichtel and Sachs, was sensible. In late 1972, it introduced a relatively conservative engine, producing only thirty-five horsepower, which had been fully tested over the previous years, and was a deliberately overengineered effort to ensure that the customers could not complain that this rotary snowmobile, the most expensive on the market at $1,850, was in any way unreliable. It had the ideal combination for breathing purposes of both peripheral and side ports—the side were open for low speeds; both were used for high speeds. OMC was not prepared to accept the roughness of a "European idle," the consistent result of only having peripheral ports, as NSU and Daimler-Benz had found. The trochoid housing was lined with tungsten carbide, a very hard substance that was very hard-wearing when combined with cast iron apex seals. But tungsten carbide is expensive stuff and was extraordinarily difficult to apply. Originally, it cost five dollars a square inch to put on, and with seventy-seven square inches to spray in a single unit, the cost was horrendous. Then a system of "plasma spraying," in which a powder is sprayed through an electric arc at such high temperatures that it is reduced to high-speed molecules which adhere to the trochoid surface, was developed by Metco, a small company in upstate New York. Today, says OMC, "The method costs pennies, but since it isn't a patent, merely our hard-earned know-how, we ain't going to tell anyone else how we do it."

All along, OMC could rely on a good deal of in-house manufacturing know-how. It had its own die-casting facilities to produce the sophisticated shape required of a Wankel rotor and made its own ignition equipment.

From a sales and marketing point of view, the rotary snowmobile was a great success. Whether OMC actually made money on the 5,000 or so rotary snowmobiles it produced (a sixth of its total output) is another matter.

A year later, OMC produced a new rotary engine, modestly introduced in the sales literature as "the even hotter HUMMER" (the name allegedly given by its customers to the first OMC rotary). The new engine was "ready to make even more beautiful, powerful, mellow music than its predecessor." OMC dodged the problem of undermining sales of the first model by keeping the earlier, less powerful engine on sale and calling the units "two HUMMERS: hot and hotter."

Because of OMC's original conservatism, it was able to increase the power of its engine by over twenty-five percent without changing the fundamental design. The engine was simply allowed to draw in gas and air for a longer period of the combustion cycle.

Today, OMC is still making only a few thousand rotary-engined snowmobiles, but its efforts and the 1972 Wankel boom in the United

States forced its biggest rival in the outboard market, the Brunswick Corporation, to take out a Wankel license in the summer of 1972. In 1974, Brunswick, like so many U.S. companies, is playing down its efforts to produce an engine, claiming that its rotary plans are of no great importance.

These "unimportant" plans will have to be upgraded if OMC puts on the market any of the marine rotaries it has been developing. The quality of these engines was dramatically demonstrated when OMC entered a number of boats equipped with water-cooled four-rotor outboard rotary engines in several speedboat races in early 1973. There had been a "sneak preview" of the engines. In February 1973, these boats were previewed for the first time in Miami's 35,000-seat marine stadium as part of the International Boat Show. The rotaries easily outperformed some of OMC's most famous high-speed reciprocating units, reaching speeds of over 100 mph. But two weeks later, in their first race, the nine-hour Enduro Race at Parker Dam in Arizona, the rotaries first misfired on the "start-your-engines" signal, then overtook the whole field within a few miles, but finally conked out altogether.

Much to OMC's relief, the trouble was traced, not to anything in the rotary itself, but to a defect in the fuel system that could have happened in a reciprocating engine.

In April, the rotary proved worthy of OMC's faith by taking the first three places in the Galveston Speed Classic in Texas. The whole boating world was astonished. If you believe in ghosts, then surely the spirit of Roy Hurley must have been at Galveston, applauding, that April day. For OMC, thirteen years late, was proving the point he had tried to make: that a dramatically fast rotary-powered boat was the finest possible advertisement for the engine.

But in outboards, as in snowmobiles, the narrow arguments over cost and bulk between the Wankel and its rivals are likely to be overwhelmed within a few years by the environmental battle. Despite OMC's success in making a two-stroke reciprocating-engined snowmobile quiet enough to satisfy even the most stringent regulations, the two-stroke engine is basically a dirty and inefficient unit. Already there is a ground swell of opposition to snowmobiles on the grounds of noise.

Then there is pollution. Already the federal government's Environmental Protection Agency, responsible for setting and policing pollution standards on cars, is asking for the authority to do the same on off-highway vehicles, whether they run on snow, water, or sand. By the end of the decade, the balance of advantage will have switched against the two-stroke engine, whose expense and bulk (like that of the ordinary petrol auto engine) will have been increased by the bolt-on contrivances it will need to cope with pollution requirements. It is at that point that the investment and hard work by farsighted pioneers such as OMC, Fichtel and Sachs, and Yanmar should really pay off.

15

Cole

"The record of technological stagnation in the automotive industry is probably unparalleled. The last significant innovation was the introduction of automatic transmission in the late 1930s, the important component of which was invented by Fottinger in 1904 and used in London buses as early as 1926."

—Yura Arkus Duntov, in testimony to U.S. Senate subcommittee on the role of the giant corporations

At around midnight on November 10, 1970, three men sat drinking champagne in the office of the president of General Motors—in itself an unusual occurrence, since the offices of GM, under normal circumstances, are strictly dry. But these were not normal circumstances. The champagne was being drunk by Ed Cole, the GM president, Gunther Henn, and Ernst Hutzenlaub of NSU in celebration of the signing of one of the most important contracts in motoring history. After eight years of investigation, GM had agreed to pay $50 million for the rights to manufacture the Wankel engine.

For GM the celebration was merely a gesture; after all, by GM's standards the money was not enormous, and the license involved no commitment to actual production of the engine. It only showed that GM, by popular repute the most conservative company in a technologically unadventurous industry, was prepared to try something new, developed outside of the company.

But for the Wankel, the GM license agreement was a landmark, the most important in its history since the first rotary engine had run sixteen years before. Until GM signed up, the Wankel could, with some reason, be dismissed as a novelty, a toy, suitable perhaps for

164

model airplanes or cars made by eccentric Japanese or philosophic Frenchmen, but not necessarily a part of the mainstream of automotive development. GM's $50 million seal of approval legitimized the engine and put the Wankel knockers on the defensive for the first time. It took them several years to rally their forces again.

GM is generally thought of as the epitome of the impersonal corporation; its founder, Alfred P. Sloan, went out of his way to paint it as such in his autobiographical work on GM. But Peter Drucker, in his review of *My Years with General Motors,* pointed out that Sloan's biggest single success lay not in the creation of the great GM corporate machine, but in his ability to handle the very difficult characters who came to work for General Motors.

It was this ability of GM to contain the occasional maverick even now, almost twenty years after Sloan left, that explains its acceptance of the Wankel. For the contract was signed on GM's behalf not by a faceless corporate bureaucrat, but by an executive who would have stood out as a distinct personality in any corporation.

Ed Cole, like many other distinguished executives in GM's history, is an engineer. But, unlike most of the others, he has been decidedly controversial, a man deeply adored, but also deeply distrusted by some of his colleagues, a personality, like so many others in the Wankel story, about whom it is impossible to be neutral. It is safe to say that without him, GM would never have taken out a Wankel license. And however enthusiastic his successors may be about the rotary, his retirement in November 1974 removed a crucial driving force in GM's development of the Wankel.

Cole started his GM career in 1930, in the depths of the depression. Like so many other Midwestern teen-agers, instead of going to college, he went to the GM Institute, the company's own university, as a student sponsored by Cadillac. He was taken away from the Institute by Cadillac before graduation, because he had already been noted as a highly promising engineer. But, in GM's cautious way with even its ablest young men, it was sixteen years before he was made Cadillac's chief engineer. Then he moved swiftly upward, first as the chief engineer of the Chevrolet division, then as its manager. By the early 1960s, he had become vice-president in charge of all GM's car and truck operations; after a spell in charge of international operations, he became, in November 1967, GM's number-two man as president, first under James Roche, then Richard Gerstenberg as chairman. But the pattern of his career and ideas had been set during his time at Cadillac, where he had been at the heart of the two major technical innovations that dominated GM in the twenty years after the war—the change to automatic transmission and the switch from older engines to more modern overhead-valve designs. These were a legacy of the only major technical figure in GM's history, Sloan's protégé, Charles Kettering, the inventor of the self-starter and much else.

When Cole joined it in the thirties, GM was a major innovative force, thanks partly to Sloan's enlightened patronage of Kettering, not only in the development of automobiles but in the whole world of mass-produced consumer durables, and a far cry from the technologically inert mass it was later to appear. Cole was at Cadillac at the same time as Earl Thompson, the developer of the syncromesh gearbox, who was working on the principles of automatic gear changing, later to become the Hydra-Matic box. At GM's central laboratories in that period was concentrated the group around Kettering that had produced Freon, the inert gas used in all modern refrigerators, and tetraethyl lead, the fuel additive which made possible the use of modern high-compression auto engines. In Cole's early years with GM, Kettering's group was combining electric and diesel motors to produce the diesel-electric engines which revolutionized railroad locomotives and swept the century-old steam locomotive off the world's railroad tracks within a generation.

So Cole was a throwback to an earlier and more glamorous age in GM's history, when GM was run by a man who did not think only of the next quarter's balance sheet. And Cole always wanted to be an innovator, and not merely a developer. Even as president of GM, he still took out numerous individual patents of his own every year; he had always been interested in novelty, sometimes, his critics would say, purely for its own sake. While still at Cadillac during the late 1940s, he had helped design a number of engines, including the revolutionary Cadillac V-8 of 1949, which set the pace for twenty years of engine design within GM and for the whole of Detroit. But the engine's development had been taken over by Kettering, then nearing the end of his career; Cole had never got the full credit for this work, and he resented the fact.

From the forties or he clearly wanted to be associated with the new and revolutionary, his motives a mixture of genuine engineering enthusiasm and a desire to be recognized, as he had not been earlier in his career. But to his critics, unaware of his earlier work, all his subsequent enthusiasms seemed to be mere gimmicks, and he himself a mere "Michigan farmer" who enjoyed tinkering with his mechanical toys, not an engineer of any depth of thought.

The first evidence of what some observers considered his unsound approach was that most controversial of vehicles, the Chevrolet Corvair, the car Ralph Nader made famous in *Unsafe at Any Speed.* The Corvair, like all Cole's ideas, was deeply personal. It could be defended as a brave attempt to tackle the dual problems of size and weight in a technically advanced way. With its uncompromisingly rectangular shape (the same NSU had used so successfully for the Prinz) and its air-cooled aluminum engine tucked away at the rear, it was the first technically original car produced by the U.S. industry since World War II. And Ed Cole's defenders could say that even the infamous swing axle, which provided Nader with his main point of attack, was featured in the Volkswagen, designed by the great Dr. Porsche himself, whose technical reputation has not suffered as a result.

From the time the Corvair was launched, Cole became a controversial figure, and nothing he did subsequently dimmed the argument. For instance, he spent a lot of time championing the inflatable air bag as a major weapon in the battle for increased road safety, while others saw it only as a dangerous gimmick. He was equally passionate about the catalytic converter as the cure-all for pollution. To many engineers it seemed merely a palliative, cleaning up the results of imperfect combustion, not curing the trouble at its source. And, eighteen months before his retirement was due, he gave his personal backing to another controversial notion. He helped finance a small independent outfit promoting a newly developed superjumbo aircraft as the first major airborne freight carrier.

In his manner he also harked back to an earlier, blunter era of Detroit executives when the motor industry did not necessarily try to placate public criticism. When he was, for instance, attacked during congressional hearings over the defective mountings of some GM engines, he simply said that they would provide no problem for expert drivers. To his numerous enemies, he was, like Denning Pearson at Rolls-Royce and Roy Hurley at Curtiss-Wright, "an engineer without a boss," that most dangerous of corporate animals. To his friends and colleagues, he was a genuinely original and enthusiastic engineer, of the type regrettably rare in the high management of GM. Because of who he was, Cole's backing of the Wankel made it inevitably a controversial project within the corporation, especially among those who felt that Cole's backing was the result of personal vanity and the desire to be a second Kettering, rather than of a genuinely objective engineering enthusiasm. Certainly, from the outside, it is very difficult to tell which motive predominated in Cole's mind.

Cole was not, however, the first senior executive in Detroit to look seriously at the Wankel. Hurley had worked for Ford, and early in 1960 Ford engineers came to Curtiss-Wright to study the engine. Max Bentele, for one, is convinced that had Hurley remained at Curtiss-Wright, Ford, whom he had worked for, would have taken out a license.

Even after Hurley's departure from Curtiss-Wright, Ford's interest continued. NSU expected a deal to be forthcoming when a squad of senior Ford executives visited Neckarsulm in 1961. For its part, Curtiss-Wright had already installed an RC 2-60 engine in a Mustang and showed it off to the motoring public. To one ecstatic motoring writer, this demonstration car "sounded almost like a six-cylinder piston engine at idle and almost like a gas turbine at speed," when, of course, the sound level did not increase. The car contained a 185-hp rotary engine, which was, in fact, somewhat slower than the 200-bhp V-8 with which the Wankel was being compared. This difference was largely due to a highly unsuitable automatic transmission that changed gears at speeds perfectly satisfactory for a conventional engine but hopelessly wrong for a Wankel.

Ford, however, was not overenthusiastic and soon concentrated on getting the price down for a license. In 1961, the asking price was a fraction of what was demanded a few years later. The top was something under the $15 million being asked of GM, the bottom the $1 million for which American Motors could have got one. Ford was asked to pay $10 million, the price, recalls one observer bitterly, "of developing half a fender." But Ford's reasoning was that only $7 million had so far been spent on developing the engine overall. To pay $10 million more was, therefore, clearly unreasonable. In addition, what Ford wanted to buy was an already developed package, with the same degree of refinement and reliability as existing competitive reciprocating engines. Ford was "not impressed by its [the Wankel's] fuel economy and its rough idling characteristics," fairly superficial criticisms of what was then a barely developed engine. By then Hurley had left Curtiss-Wright, and his successors did not help the sales effort by insisting that Ford be allowed only to test the engine in a car and not strip it down for examination or subject it to proper tests on a dynamometer. So there was no real reason for Ford to go out of its way to pay for a mystery package which contained merely what one senior Ford man described as a "Mickey Mouse of an engine."

The situation at Chrysler was somewhat more hopeful, especially as there was an engineer from Daimler-Benz on its engineering staff who took the Wankel very seriously. The fourth U.S. motor manufacturer, American Motors, was not at the time a potential customer. It was perennially short of cash and in any case was busy developing another alternative engine, the Cooley, in conjunction with the French Renault company.

Chrysler, too, was also developing an alternative source of power, the gas turbine. At the time, this appeared to be both more promising and more glamorous than the Wankel (to belong to the Wankel set does not, somehow, sound as exciting as belonging to the jet set). During 1962, Chrysler was demonstrating a turbine-engined Dodge Dart and the next year showed its confidence in the engine by issuing fifty of them to the public for a two-year free trial.

There was one further clinching argument against the Wankel —timidity, the unwillingness to follow where GM had not led. "Be reasonable," said Harry Cheeseborough, then Chrysler's chief engineer, to a Wankel enthusiast. "How can we do it if GM hasn't?"

The man whom Cheeseborough was addressing was a Russian-born engineer, Yura Arkus Duntov, a crucial figure in the Wankel story, who, like Lindenmayr and Bentele, has been ill-rewarded for his contribution. Duntov had fled through Europe in the 1920s and 1930s, was educated in Belgium, and had landed in the United States where, in the late 1950s, he worked for Hurley at Curtiss-Wright. After a spell trying to make some sense of the administrative chaos of the Wankel program, he had left the firm in disgust. After Hurley's departure, he had been invited back by the new management. By then he had been taken on by the Dreyfus Fund as the mutual fund's first specialist adviser on the scientific and technological aspects of investment. Nevertheless, he put his gentle, silver-tongued Slavonic charm at the service of selling the Wankel to Detroit, providing a link, for instance, to the Morgan Guaranty Trust that had first encouraged Ford to take an interest in the engine.

Duntov was fully aware of the problem posed by Cheeseborough's remark. "We needed GM and we needed a champion within GM." By a happy accident, he was able to provide the link. Before his retirement in 1974, Duntov's brother Zora had worked for two decades developing and perfecting the Chevrolet Corvette, GM's prestige sports car, produced in tiny quantities (a mere 25,000 or so a year) but at enormous profit to show that the Chevrolet name could be attached to vehicles that were, by U.S. standards, exciting to drive.

Zora, ironically, has never been very keen on the Wankel. But he provided a contact between his brother and Cole, who had been his boss for some years. By early 1962, Cole was eagerly writing to Duntov wanting to get hold of one of the new engines. This was easier said than done. For the request threw NSU into something of a dither. While it desperately wanted to forge this link with GM, it did not want to offend Curtiss-Wright, especially as it was in the middle of legal proceedings trying to rewrite the license agreement anyway.

To make matters worse, the current version of the KKM 502 engine running in a specially adapted Prinz test car was having problems with its apex seals. So (much to Cole's enjoyment) a test vehicle was virtually smuggled to Cole in the summer of that year via GM's subsidiaries, Opel in Germany, and Vauxhall in Britain. At the same time, Curtiss-Wright was supplying a single-rotor test engine through more orthodox channels to GM's technical center for evaluation—on the strict understanding that GM would only test the engine and not try to discover its secrets by dismantling it.

GM's Engine Department was not enthusiastic about the rotary. It was reluctant to admit "that some small German outfit could have thought of something which had never occurred to GM." Nevertheless, because of Cole's enthusiasm, the engine was put on a stand and thoroughly tested, where its major disadvantage soon became apparent. Quite literally, "it stank." No wonder that in Detroit in the early 1960s the Wankel acquired the name of "the little engine that couldn't"—it seemed that its smoky exhaust could not be curbed; it could not match the fuel economy of orthodox engines; and, most damningly from Detroit's point of view, it could not be mass-produced.

The combustion process in the Wankel was still something of a mystery. It was clear only that the rotary did not burn fuel as efficiently as a conventional engine. The ever-changing, elongated shape of its combustion chamber prevents the "swirl" which helps ignition in modern conventional engines, and the flat shape "quenches" the flame. Compared with conventional engines, the combustion temperature is low and the process relatively incomplete. As a result, the emission of two of the three major sources of automotive pollution—carbon monoxide (CO) and hydrocarbons (HC)—is higher; for the more efficient the combustion process in an engine, the greater the percentage of these pollutants that are burned up. But precisely the opposite is true of the third and most obdurate pollutant, the various oxides of nitrogen (generally known as NO_x). These form in the leading edge of the flame as it advances through the gas-and-air mixture; they are affected by the temperature and pressure of combustion. The Wankel's relatively slow and gentle combustion process does not encourage the formation of these gases; so it emits at least a third less NO_x than a conventional engine—an advantage *parallel* to the disadvantage it suffers with CO and HC.

However, NO_x had not been identified as a separate problem when pollution first worried Detroit in the mid-1960s. For Ford and Chrysler, this objective inferiority of the rotary to the reciprocal engine was a good reason to abandon serious consideration of the engine. It also provided a check to the dreams of Duntov and Cole. It was thought at the time that the pollutants in an automobile's exhaust could be curbed by tinkering with the carburetion, timing, and mixture of reciprocating engines which, up till then, had not been designed to minimize pollution but to produce the best possible performance.

Duntov and Cole were less sure that mechanical adjustments would suffice. Cole was an early believer in the system of catalytic conversion to solve the emissions problem. In this technique, the exhaust fumes are passed through a chamber containing a catalyst (a substance which causes chemical change without itself changing). At the time, this solution seemed unnecessarily costly and complicated. But Duntov was convinced that it would prove to be necessary in the future and that·the Wankel could more easily be hooked up with such a chamber than an ordinary engine. In the words of William Figart of Curtiss-Wright:

For years Detroit thought it could solve the problems of emissions by tinkering with the inside of the piston engine—adjusting the timing of the carburetion, adding positive control valves, and the like. But then they realized that they were going to be forced to the outside of the engine if they were to reduce emissions to the federally required levels. They saw that they would have to add a reactor or a converter to the exhaust. And that is where the disadvantages of the Wankel, with its high temperatures (of the exhaust gases) and high level of CO and HCs, actually became advantages. These are all ideal conditions for a converter, for example, because they cause the catalyst to heat up rapidly and hasten the complete oxidization of the exhaust. And in addition, the Wankel has the advantage of its small size and simplicity.

By then Duntov clearly believed that without his help Curtiss-Wright would not get anywhere with GM. "It is quite apparent," he wrote to Cole, "that CW has made the least amount of progress with GM." The only hope was personal persuasion. So he negotiated an agreement with Curtiss-Wright and NSU in 1965 which gave him the right to three percent of any revenue from licenses negotiated through him within the next couple of years. In a master stroke of personal psychology, he proposed that Cole's son David, then a very young professor at the University of Michigan, undertake research on the pollution problems of the Wankel. The Automobile Department of the university at Ann Arbor was one of the country's best and was only twenty-five miles from Detroit.

Cole was amused by the suggestion, but it took a year to persuade Curtiss-Wright and NSU that the giant fish GM could be lured with the expenditure of a mere $50,000 on pollution research into the Wankel net. NSU was worried at setting a precedent and upsetting its still tender relationship with Curtiss-Wright, an attitude which drove Duntov near to despair. As he wrote in a letter to von Heyde-kampf, "There is some kind of mysterious lethargy which affects anyone who is connected with the Wankel engine."

The study, therefore, did not start until 1966, and the report was not finished until November 1967, the same month Ed Cole was appointed to GM's number-two job. The delay in starting the research proved not fatal to the engine's prospects. In fact, by 1968 it was becoming increasingly clear that mere adjustments would not be enough to handle exhaust pollutants to the public satisfaction. But the delay did prevent Duntov from benefiting from the eventual license. His agreement with Curtiss-Wright and NSU was not renewed, and he has only a moral claim to the $1.5 million his percentage would have amounted to.

David Cole's report showed that the very qualities that made the Wankel so unsuitable for mere tinkering made it highly suitable for the more drastic treatment which was increasingly becoming necessary to meet pollution requirements.

Because combustion always takes place at the same point on the epitrochoid housing, the exhaust ports never have the chance to get cool, whereas in an orthodox engine the whole combustion chamber is cooled by the incoming charge of gas and air before the next charge is ignited. So the exhaust gases on a Wankel are hotter than on an orthodox engine even though the actual temperature of combustion is lower. This contrast, as David Cole and his colleagues showed convincingly, made the Wankel an ideal engine on which to try either (or both) of the basic units being developed for meeting the pollution requirements envisioned in the late 1960s—far stricter than had been thought necessary or practicable even a few years previously. The two methods both involved bolt-on converter units attached to the exhaust system. They were the catalytic reactor and a thermal reactor. The latter depended on a stream of fresh air injected into the exhaust, which mixed with the exhaust gases, started them burning again, and thus completed the combustion process.

Cole and his fellow researchers also found that the Wankel was at its dirtiest at low speeds and while warming up. But with a relatively crude thermal reactor attached to the engine's exhaust port, emissions were reduced by a half, and by up to three-quarters when its effects were reinforced by injecting a stream of fresh air into the short length of pipe connecting the exhaust port to the reactor. The fresh air mixed with the partially burned hydrocarbons in the exhaust mixture, and together they completed the combustion process. What is more, the process worked efficiently only half a minute after the engine was started up—a major advantage over reciprocating engines, where a crucial problem was the very high level of pollutants emitted during the first few minutes while the engine was warming up.

David Cole's report showed that the very qualities that made the and the looming threat of federal pollution control kept the impetus for a license going during a two-and-a-half-year hiatus. It soon became clear to Henn and Hutzenlaub, who were conducting the negotiations, that GM would be no ordinary licensee and that the standard license package which Henn had devised (described in Chapter —) was entirely inappropriate. GM was interested only in the basic coverage needed to manufacture Wankel engines before the patents filed by NSU expired at the end of the 1970s. GM was also interested in getting the know-how acquired by the licensees up to the time it bought its license. But it was obviously determined to go its own way from that point. It was *not* interested in acquiring the rights to the hundreds of patents filed by licensees. It was not prepared to be a good member of the Wankel Club and share its knowledge and inventions with other licensees. It wanted a license unbounded by geographical or product limitations. And it was not interested in paying royalties on every engine it might produce—naturally enough, since its Chevrolet division alone produced 2 million cars a year, more than all the existing licensees put together.

Technical pride and fear of the Department of Justice's Antitrust Division also played a part in limiting GM's involvement with the license owners. It was only because of the patent situation that it was prepared to admit the need for a license at all. The Department of Justice was already investigating work done jointly by the motor companies on pollution and safety problems. And GM naturally feared that any continuing association with the other licensees would lead to more investigations—a worry which had prevented GM from buying up Wankel G.m.B.h. itself.

The urgency of the discussions ebbed and flowed with the progress of antipollution legislation. When a Clean Air Act of some sort became inevitable, the talks became more serious. When the bill got stuck in congressional committees, the doubters within GM got their chance to discount the need for the engine and get tougher on the terms. Richard Gerstenberg ("Ole Dick the bookkeeper," as he described himself), the designated successor to Roche for the top job, succeeded in amending the original idea of a lump sum to a series of payments, which gave GM time to withdraw before committing itself totally and irrevocably.

By the summer of 1970, however, it was clear that some form of agreement among Wankel G.m.B.h, NSU, and GM would emerge. There were even press rumors that talks were being conducted through GM's German subsidiary, Adam Opel, to buy Wankel g.m.b.h. itself to give GM forty percent of all the license revenues. At the lengthy and well-publicized Annual General Meeting of Audi-NSU in June 1970, Henn admitted as much, possibly as a way of stirring up interest in the engine. GM was forced to admit in a press release that "discussions are being held with Wankel g.m.b.h. as part of our stated policy of investigating all possible sources of auto-motive power."

The next month a decisive step was taken. Robert Templin, a former Cadillac engineer, was appointed to take charge of GM's rotary engine program. GM had been working at an increasing intensity on the engine for a number of years, but Templin's ap-pointment legitimized the situation.

By early December 1970, all was settled. An agreement was announced on November 3 and signed on November 10—the day Cole, Henn, Hutzenlaub were in Cole's office drinking champagne.

The agreement that was signed satisfied both sides. From GM's point of view, the total cost of the license, $50 million, was a fabulous bargain, even though the sums involved were far greater than had been discussed a few years before when the engine was first being touted around Detroit. GM acquired nonexclusive rights to man-ufacture the Wankel for sale anywhere it liked and for any use except in aircraft. It got the rights to all the patents owned by Audi-NSU and to any further ones "based on inventions conceived prior to the date of this agreement." It could use the Wankel in any "compressor, blower, expansion engine" and could sell them anywhere in the world. There was no mention of royalties or sharing any discoveries which GM might make and patent in the field. For GM to take out a license would clearly enhance the engine's worldwide standing. GM knew this and used the fact as an extremely effective lever to get the best possible terms for its license.

Gerstenberg's caution was reflected in the timing of the payments. Five million dollars was payable immediately. Then four successive payments of $10 million were to be made annually on or before December 26, starting in 1971. At the end of 1975, a final payment of $5 million was due. GM had only to give one day's notice if at any point it decided it did not want to continue the payment and to terminate the agreement.

The sums due were divided: Six-elevenths were to go to Audi-NSU and Wankel and five-elevenths to Curtiss-Wright. But when the idea of a once-for-all lump sum payment was abandoned, Henn continued to outsmart GM. He insisted that the money being paid to the Germans should be expressed in Deutsche marks. So they were; subsequent revaluations of the German currency (and devaluation of the dollar) have considerably increased the dollar amount GM is paying for the license. The first $10 million payment in December 1971 cost in fact over $10.6 million, the second $10.75 million, the third $11.9 million, and if the whole amount is paid as originally planned, the total would have been over $58 million rather than the $50 million agreed at the time. Ole Dick's bookkeeping has cost GM dear.

The underlying reasoning behind the GM decision was spotted in the motor industry's monthly magazine, *Ward's Auto World,* by Richard Waddell (who now admits that he did not realize how right he was). In January 1971, he wrote that "weight sums up the automotive engineering fraternity's chief challenge for the 1970s. In one way or another, it figures into safety, emissions, repairability, and styling, and it reaches deeply into materials and manufacturing processes."

A year before, Cole had spelled out the reasons that made it inevitable at the Society of Automotive Engineers' annual banquet, one of the high spots of the industry's year. In his speech he named as one of his priorities for the 1970s "better concepts of space engineering. As the customer demands more and more of the automobile, we must seek new ways of maximizing the use of space available both in exterior dimensions and under the skin of the car." "The customer," he added, "certainly isn't getting any smaller."

At the same banquet, he admitted that there were definite limitations on the size of the car "imposed by such vital factors as highway and parking space."

Three years later Cole spelled out the figures. New components needed to conform with safety and pollution regulations would add

400 to 600 pounds to the weight of a car. "Weight is significant. We say on a given car 400 pounds of weight increase comes to nearly one mile per gallon."

The average miles per gallon of the basic Ford line declined from fifteen in 1967 to a mere eleven and a half five years later, helped downward by the war against polluting emissions. "Compact" cars grew in size, although it was gradually dawning on the U.S. motorist that overall size had little to do with the room inside the car. Sales of European middle-sized cars—Mercedes, Volvo, Audi—were booming. For the first time, European auto packaging could be fairly compared with American. Previously, most European-built cars sold in the United States, like the VW Beetle, were not competing directly with any American vehicles. The results of the comparison were startling. The Audi 100LS, being vigorously marketed by VW, weighed 2,582 pounds and did twenty miles to the gallon. The Oldsmobile Omega, half a ton heavier, a foot longer, with an engine three times the size, did only eleven miles per gallon, yet had less leg and shoulder room and a smaller trunk than the European car.

The lighter weight and smaller bulk of the Wankel is especially significant on bigger cars of over 200 bhp, of which GM is the world's major producer—for this size engine even the conservative Ludvigsen reckoned the saving as eleven percent in weight and thirty percent in bulk, compared to a reciprocating engine of equal power. But all these points would not by themselves have been adequate to induce GM to commit itself to investing heavily in an imported invention. Ideas less controversial in their field and more unarguably superior than the Wankel, ranging from front-wheel drive to disk brakes and radial-ply tires, had been resisted by Detroit decades after they had become standard equipment on small European cars, because they added a few dollars to the price of a car or made it more complicated to produce, or, as with the front-wheel drive, both. It was not technical ignorance on Detroit's part—the Toronado made by GM's Oldsmobile division was by far the heaviest and biggest car ever produced with front-wheel drive—but the all-pervasive and relentless pressure of the short-term profit situation that kept the engineers in check. And even an engineer as forceful and as highly placed as Cole could not, in the end, argue with the dollars-and-cents men.

So the Wankel would not have been accepted if it had not been potentially simpler and cheaper to produce as well as smaller and lighter than existing units. But it arrived at an appropriate time, when the great burst of technological improvement which came with the high-performance engines of the 1950s and 1960s had worked its way through to virtually every GM car; when, in a parallel feat of production engineering, the cost of producing these engines had been dramatically reduced—about sixty percent of the labor cost of producing a standard V-8 engine had been removed in the fifteen years after 1955. Cole was referring to production technology on existent units when he said to the group of import investors that "the possibility for further technological improvements in our business is not as great as in the past."

What led GM to invest its money in the Wankel was listed in a report by Templin delivered in early 1972 at an open day for leading institutional investors at the GM technical center, a lavishly equipped group of elegant Saarinen-designed buildings west of Detroit. In GM's "1972 report on progress in areas of public concern," Templin listed as an asset of the rotary its size: a 200-cubic-inch rotary would be substantially smaller than the Vega four-cylinder unit, the smallest in GM's range, but would be comparable in power to the standard six-cylinder production engine and thirty percent lighter. This weight and bulk difference is desirable now, the report said, and essential later in the 1970s because of the bulkiness of what would be mandatory pollution devices. Developing a rotary-powered automobile is "the only way we know to simultaneously improve fuel economy, vehicle performance, and emissions." It was, Templin added, the same point Cole had made two years before: Market research had shown that demand "for smaller, more functional vehicles is increasing, a demand that can best be met by more efficient vehicle designs, possibly using rotary combustion engines."

But Templin went nearer the heart of GM's worries about the future than the ritual obeisance in favor of smaller vehicles. The Wankel had fewer parts, which in theory permitted even greater automation and standardization than GM had already achieved with reciprocating units. "The rotary combustion engine permits a wide range of engine displacements to be built by varying the width of a single chamber or using one, two, or even three rotors." He went on to mention the inherent smoothness of the rotary engine, and finally, and without undue emphasis, he noted the pollution element in the Wankel package.

In this seemingly rational analysis, one element is missing—Cole's own desire, at the end of a successful career, to immortalize himself by pushing through a revolution in automative engineering for which he could get the credit, as Kettering had done for the engines Cole himself had done so much to design.

The license was signed on December 10, 1970. From that moment on, GM has put up an iron curtain between the public and its development activities.

Journalists (including this author) have been denied official access to those involved in the Wankel program at GM, even if only to discuss its technical background or historical aspects. Consequently, any account of the history of the engine inside the fortress of GM is as difficult to compile as an account of the inner workings of the CIA. This is not too grotesque an exaggeration. The final security document issued to all GM senior executives in October 1972 on the subject of the Wankel starts grimly enough. "Strict security," it says, "is essential to the successful operation of our business."

"Careless disclosure, even if unwitting, is detrimental, not only to the best interests of the corporation and its stockholders, but to the best interests of employees themselves, in a direct and personal way."

This warning was amplified later in a passage about the importance of not profiting from any leakage of confidential material. "Use of such information for the benefit of an employee is a violation of the obligation of an employee to his employer."

GM warned its employees that even if the corporation chose not to prosecute the guilty party, the shareholders could. In conclusion, "Publicity material in connection with new plants and plant improvements must be approved by the president or vice-chairman as appropriate, before release." In other words, Cole himself as president had to approve all press releases on the subject of the Wankel personally.

The corporation's public relations staff took their instructions seriously enough. "Let me see," said one in response to a query about the engine. "I can give you the titles of some magazine articles that might help you out." Even within the company, rotary plans were confidential. Inquiries by one GM executive as to whether his range of cars would be equipped with rotary engines "were met with a good, strong 'maybe.' "

Fortunately, GM's executives are not inhuman; they drink and they chat. Fortunately, too, GM had to involve hundreds of component suppliers who, proud of their achievements in helping to make the Wankel a workable proposition, were less inclined than GM to maintain strict security, especially when talking to their friends in the technical and trade press. Cole and Templin were not entirely silent either; when they were cornered at the end of formal press conferences, and on the way to airports, they gave short, cryptic interviews. While the program was going well, GM was not too unhappy if details leaked out in the automotive press (the deliberate leak, in this case to titillate public interest in a project which does not compete with an existing range of cars, is a well-known technique in selling as well as in politics). Without relying on defectors or electronic aids, it is possible to build up a fair picture of the engine's progress through the GM development machine.

After the license was signed, the engine was no longer a Wankel. It became and remained the GMRE—General Motors Rotary Engine. The engine was now a GM project. It was to be built, not by one of the car manufacturer divisions, nor yet by an engine manufacturer within GM, but by the Hydra-Matic Division. This division was only responsible for building automatic transmissions. But the manufacture of the Wankel most closely resembled the production of automatic transmissions. Both involved the machining of complicated *curved* parts and fitting them around a central shaft on a scale and to a degree of exactitude not even attempted elsewhere in any GM plant.

As John Z. De Lorean, then head of Chevrolet, said, "I think it is fortunate for us that they [Hydra-Matic Division] are the supplier because the engine does have many characteristics of an automatic transmission from the type of machinery and the design of it." This was not a universally shared view of the motor, however. There were many others at Chevrolet who disagreed and thought they, not Hydra-Matic, should be building the engine.

Another reason for choosing a division that had never produced reciprocating engines or vehicles to develop the GMRE was that Hydra-Matic personnel would have no vested interest to prove that the new idea would not work, or any preconceived notion as to how rotaries should be developed.

Twenty years before, Hydra-Matic, then called Detroit Transmissions, had been set up by Alfred P. Sloan, Jr., as a separate division to carry through the last great technical revolution in GM's history before the Wankel, the production of automatic transmissions on a scale to make them part of everyday motoring. The comparison with the Wankel was natural. Dave Smith, editor of *Ward's Auto World* and one of Detroit's leading automotive writers, specifically called the rotary engine "the biggest thing to hit Detroit since the automatic transmission."

Hydra-Matic would produce the engine, but only if and when the decision was made to turn from development to production. The design of the rotary and preproduction development were a matter for Templin and his group within GM's Central Engineering Development Department—again a departure from GM's historic norm. But in the late 1960s, Cole had transformed a well-ordered if meek group ("which spoke only when it was asked") into a number of fluid project teams able to concentrate hundreds of specialist engineers on a given problem. These teams could also call on GM's specialist divisions, for example those making carburetors and ignition equipment. This managerial reorganization helped to ensure that rotary development would incorporate as many advanced GM ideas as possible and would therefore be a real showpiece of GM's engineering prowess.

Templin needed all the help he could get, for originally it was hoped to produce an engine—albeit in small numbers—for the 1974 model year, less than three years after the license agreement had been signed. The time scale for the design and production of even a new conventional engine is longer than that. What is more—the pioneer GM rotary had to compete head on with existing engines.

In the words of Karl Ludvigsen, Templin had "to bring it into line with the new emission levels, fuel economy, and the power per cubic inch of the best present production engines."

Templin started by testing the only two existing rotary engines used in cars, the Mazda and the unhappy RO80 unit, and then designing the simplest possible motor. At this point in GM's rotary plans, its ideas were pretty radical. Unlike the Mazda, the GMRE was to have only one spark plug instead of two—and no fuel injection.

Unlike the Mazda and all other production engines, the crucial rotor housing was to be cheap cast iron and not expensive aluminum. And since some of the GM engines were designed to be mounted vertically, like those on a rotary lawn mower, even the oil sump was not necessarily in its usual place below the engine. However, GM did copy the dimensions of Mazda's rotor and the positioning of the ports. The inlet ports were on the sides of the chamber and the exhaust ports on the periphery. The Americans and the Japanese were both concerned above all with producing a practical engine and, by sticking to side inlet ports, should avoid the problems the Germans, NSU, and Daimler-Benz have experienced with the rotary at low speeds.

But GM, like everyone else connected with the engine, underestimated the problems involved in bringing the rotary into production. After all, they had even less experience with producing radically new mechanical ideas than the European manufacturers. In the preceding decade, Detroit's technological innovations had been very minor. De Lorean, for instance, when he was manager of Pontiac, had been hailed as a considerable innovator because he introduced windscreen wipers which tucked away out of sight under a fold in the car hood. No wonder one GM engineer was quoted as saying about the rotary, "At last we're working on something people want."

But it was very difficult work. The first generation of test engines built during 1971 produced too many polluting emissions and not enough power. The use of cast iron housings meant excessive heat around the combustion area. GM first put an aluminum insert at the hottest part of the engine around the spark plug; then tried casting the iron around the plug as thin as possible, but it just did not work.

Outwardly, Cole remained enthusiastic. In June 1971, "in a kind of corporate show-and-tell time," the GM directors were shown the first likely use for the engine, in a new car smaller even than the Vega, or in the Vega itself, GM's smallest U.S. production model. In December, GM went ahead with its second payment of $10 million to Wankel G.m.B.h. and NSU. It was one of the last decisions made under the retiring chairman, Jim Roche. "Even though," says Ludvigsen, "the engineering evidence wasn't very convincing, there are those in GM who feel the proposal to continue with the Wankel wouldn't have passed the muster of GM's new chairman, Richard

Gerstenberg." Gerstenberg was quoted at the time as saying, "We have been encouraged, but we haven't been able to resolve all the problems yet. People could gobble it up like mad, but it could still fall flat in the long run"—probably referring to the fate of Cole's much-heralded Corvair, whose sales were already fading when Ralph Nader's criticism provided the final blow that ended the car's controversial career.

But in the first half of 1972, development work seemed to be going better. Cole was spending two full days a week at the GM Research Center and making confident statements that "we understand the engine's combustion process," with the implication that no one before GM had. In his statement in February to GM's institutional investors, Templin stressed how far GM had got in its researches: "Fuel economy and long-lasting seals were initially serious problems." This statement invited the inference that only fifteen months after the license had been signed, these problems, generally considered the most troublesome for the engine, had already been conquered.

His optimism was echoed by the trade and motoring press, which were full of predictions that a car using a rotary engine would be in production in time for the 1974 model year—that is, starting sometime at the end of 1973. The car, it was assumed, would be a Vega, costing a hefty $3,500, with a 175-bhp engine, the prelude to a revolutionary front-wheel-drive vehicle to be introduced a year later.

A report from Washington seemed to confirm these rumors. Inspired by Cole's belief in the catalytic converter, GM was the only American car maker to maintain that its cars could satisfy the government's strict new emission standards laid down in the Clean Air Act, which had finally become law in 1971. And in April 1972, the government's Environmental Protection Agency let the rotary cat out of the bag. In a report saying why it had rejected the one-year postponement requested by Detroit for the introduction of these standards, the agency casually added that "General Motors is the only major manufacturer which plans to produce limited numbers of rotary engine vehicles in 1975."

Gerstenberg found it very hard to deny this schedule, and Cole's remark that GM needed no new breakthroughs and was "merely trying to optimize the engine" did not make it any easier. Cole's boss pointed out that there had as yet been no road testing of a rotary-engined vehicle, and there was a great difference between laboratory conditions and those in real life. What is more—GM did not know the cost of manufacturing the engine. "We don't know yet if the rotary is the engine of the future" was Gerstenberg's view.

Yet the rumors kept circulating. It was said that GM planned to sell the engine to its two weakest competitors, Chrysler and American Motors, as had been done previously with collapsible steering wheels and automatic transmissions, to avoid being charged with monopolistic trading. Almost every GM car manufacturing division was mentioned as an early customer for the rotary engine. This spate of rumors culminated in June 1972 at the annual show of future models held in GM's lavish Milford proving grounds, where the entire range of ideas Cole and his staff had developed for using the rotary engine was displayed. This show was supposed to be top secret, but inevitably details leaked out.

GM had been thinking all along in terms of a family of engines, with one, two, and three rotors, and two widths of rotor—giving two sizes of engine for each number of rotors. These combinations could produce six basic engine sizes. GM could, in theory, then replace all the engines it currently had in production by rotary units. The smallest rotary unit would be suitable for a subcompact car, where even a one-rotor unit would be superior to the very rough four-cylinder unit used in the Vega; the biggest Wankel would be marvelous for a high-powered sports car or a full-sized luxury automobile.

But the display in June 1972 was more than a pyrotechnic exhibition of engineering ingenuity and more than a demonstration of how GM could combat size, weight, and pollution problems. It also represented GM's bid to regain the fashion initiative from Ford, throughout the 1960s the pace-setter in producing new cars. The battle had begun with GM's Chevrolet Monza, a dressed-up 1961 version of Cole's Corvair. But it was Ford that capitalized on the market which the Monza had revealed, bringing out the Mustang in 1964, followed in the next few years by the Cougar, the Maverick, the Comet, and the subcompact Pinto. GM's entries in the field had either tended to be belated (like the Camaro) or much criticized (as the Vega proved to be). Ford, apart from the increasingly successful Lincoln Continental, was still unable to challenge GM seriously in the market for prestige vehicles, where Mercury was no real match for the combined weight of Buick, Oldsmobile, and Pontiac. But GM had undoubtedly lost ground among younger and more fashion-conscious buyers. The rotary revolution provided a chance for a comeback.

The reaction of the board of directors to the display was guarded, but not discouraging. "We didn't," said one cryptic observer, "hear anything that indicated they disliked what we were doing."

But the directors of GM come mostly not from inside the company but from the very different worlds of Wall Street and other industries; they would not be totally convinced by Cole's enthusiasm, however contagious. They needed evidence that rotary-engined vehicles could be made cheaply and sold at a profit, that the American car-buying public (not to mention Wall Street) was ready for the rotary. But the timing was right. In the eighteen months since Cole, Henn, and Hutzenlaub had signed the agreement, the Wankel had caught the imagination, one after the other, of the U.S. manufacturers, U.S. investors, and U.S. car buyers.

While Cole, Templin, and their engineers had been beavering away, there had been a Wankel revolution.

16

Producibility

"The rotary engine does have fewer parts, and the engineers lay them all out and say, 'See, count 'em.' And then I say, 'Okay. Now what do you think it is going to cost?' They say, 'Well, when we get to work on that. . .'"
— THOMAS A. MURPHY, vice-chairman, General Motors

The major hurdle for any new product being considered by a major U.S. motor manufacturer has always been its "producibility." One of the reasons GM had taken out a Wankel license was that it believed that the rotary would, eventually, be more economical to produce than a reciprocating engine of equivalent power.

First, the cost of each engine must be cut to the bone. The sums involved are enormous because the scale of production is so large; the standard figure for production of a single model in the United States is 500,000 a year—the amount for the plant in Lima, Ohio, where Ford produces the engines for its subcompact Pinto. The total U.S. production of automobile engines is 200,000 a week.

Because the rotary contains fewer parts to machine and assemble than a reciprocating engine, it was reasonably easy to prove that it would score. In 1972, Robert J. Perry of Babcock and Wilcox, a leading machine tool manufacturer, reckoned that tooling for a rotary would cost fifteen percent less than for conventional engines. This, in theory, would have saved Ford over $15 million on its Lima plant operations alone. But turning this theoretical advantage into practice involved two linked problems. Many of the components and processes required for the rotary had not previously been established in mass production, and some were complex enough to require special manufacturing techniques.

186

There were some components, like the ignition and the pumps, that were reasonably standard and could be produced within GM at an easily calculable price. Others, like the cast iron side housings, were not standard, but were relatively uncomplicated to manufacture. But the rotor itself, its sealing system, and the curved housing had never been made in Detroit-sized quantities. Furthermore, Toyo Kogyo's uninspired profit record since it started producing rotaries on a considerable scale, together with its unwillingness to let outsiders near certain key production areas, suggested that even the Japanese had not solved these problems.

But the GM engineers had two major advantages over Toyo Kogyo: the sheer muscle provided by GM's size and the experience accumulated by other manufacturers, notably Mercedes-Benz and Toyo Kogyo itself, during the 1960s. The Germans and the Japanese had solved the problem that had so dogged NSU—the wear on the rotor's apex seals—in two different ways. Where Toyo Kogyo, following NSU's original idea, had developed carbon seals which, hopefully, wore out at a gradual and predictable rate on the rotor's hard chrome housing, Mercedes had opted for two hard and expensive materials rubbing against each other, the nickel-based alloys Elnisil and IKA.

Consequently, GM's problem with these seals was in achieving a balance between price and durability. Some of the sealing designs GM tested lasted for the equivalent of 500,000 miles. As a first—possibly temporary—solution, GM settled for the less durable but much cheaper carbon seals for its GMRE.

Then there was the curved housing around the rotor. It had to be of cheap material and easily manufactured, yet required finishing to very exact tolerances and, even worse, to a shape with which machine-tool manufacturers were totally unfamiliar. The swollen figure-eight shape of this epitrochoid is not one circle but two, requiring a machine that would change cutting direction in midstream. In the mid-1950s, it had taken NSU a year to design a machine to to this job at all, and even fifteen years later there was no machine tool available that would grind the swollen figure eight at the speed required for mass production. To complicate the situation, GM had to accept that cast iron, its first choice, could not dissipate the heat built up by combustion quickly enough; only aluminum could. Yet an aluminum housing was not durable enough; it needed double coating: first, a thin layer of low-carbon steel, which itself had

188 · WANKEL

to be finished to strengthen it, then a layer of chrome on the inside ground to a fine enough tolerance to prevent the dreaded "chatter marks" which resulted from the rotor moving across an uneven surface.

The first of these problems—attaching a thin steel coat to the aluminum—had been solved some years before by Dr. Alfred F. Bauer, another of those German immigrant engineers who have frequently cropped up in the Wankel story. Bauer, educated in Stuttgart, had built up the biggest plant in Europe for die-casting (casting is the pouring of molten metal into some form of mold to make as exact a shape as possible). During the war, like Wankel, Bensinger, Lindenmayr, and Bentele, he had worked on projects involving applied technology, culminating with the V-2 rocket which bombed London at the end of the war. He moved to the United States in 1947 to work for the Defense Department, but, four years later, moved to a firm called Doehler-Jarvis.

There he developed and patented TPC—the transplant coat process. "Conceptually," *Ward's Wankel Report* pointed out, "the patent comes from what seems an odd-ball approach of reversing normal coating methods. An extreme analogy would be painting a house backward. First you'd put up the paint (or coating), if it would stand up of course; then you'd bond the boards to the paint."

In the TPC process, a steel core (shaped like a swollen-waisted figure eight in the case of the Wankel) is sprayed with steel and then, under pressure, the aluminum is poured in and the two interlock together. When the steel core is cooled with water, it contracts and drops out of the middle, leaving an aluminum casting lined with a coat of steel—a quarter of an inch thick in the case of Toyo Kogyo engines, less in GM's.

But there were no precedents for the three final processes in finishing the housing. First, the inner steel layer had to be finished to a tolerance of a few thousandths of an inch; then an exceedingly thin layer of chrome, a mere thousandth or two thick, had to be deposited, and finally honed.

Machine-tool manufacturers, who had been decidedly sniffy when Outboard Marine, the pioneer of Wankel manufacture in the United States, had come around looking for help, now had to set to work whether they liked it or not at the bidding of their biggest customer. The suppliers all put a brave face on it, claiming to be glad of the technical challenges (and of the potential new orders at a time when the machine tool industry as a whole was far from booming). In fact, they had no choice. John De Lorean of Chevrolet had said he thought "one of America's really great and outstanding resources is our trememdous tooling industry." GM certainly knew how to exploit this particular national resource. Indeed, even if GM had never gone into production with the rotary engine, the pressure it applied to its suppliers ensured that any other motor manufacturer would, for the first time, be able to buy a ready-made do-it-yourself Wankel production line.

The first machine tool manufacturer off the mark in the race to solve the crucial problem of machining the inside of the rotor housing was the Tri-Ordinate Corporation, a small family company run by another European immigrant engineer, Nils Hoglund, a Swedish-born inventor. In December 1970, only a month after GM had signed the license contract, Hoglund, on holiday in Florida, dreamed up a design for a grinder with three cams to cope with the housing's peculiar shape. Back home in New Jersey, he "built" the first machine and named it the Tru-Coid. According to Mrs. Hoglund, it was made "from boiler plates, shims, baling wire, and it should be a good candidate for the Smithsonian Institute."

It worked well enough to be sold to GM because it demonstrated that the rotor housings could be ground at speeds three or four times those achieved by the Tru-Coid's German competitor, the Kopp grinder. The difference between the Kopp's rate of six or seven an hour and that achieved by the American machine was just the sort of breakthrough GM, and indeed the whole Wankel engine world, needed.

It is not as extraordinary as it seems that Hoglund knew so soon about what GM was looking for. He had previously solved a similarly difficult manufacturing problem on the M16 rifle that GM was making for the U.S. Army under the direction of Wilbur Crawfurd, one of GM's band of vital master mechanics. Hoglund later provided indirect proof that Toyo Kogyo's secrecy over the methods it used to manufacture the Wankel was at least partly due to their backwardness. In 1972, when he and his wife went to Japan on what was supposed to be a private visit, they were met at the airport by a number of limousines provided by Japan's major trading companies, each more eager than the other to acquire the Japanese rights to his machines. The Hoglunds' visit rapidly turned into a triumphal progress while he decided on which corporation he would bestow his invaluable know-how. Had any Japanese firm developed a remotely competitive machine for machining the rotary housing, the welcome would presumably have been less overwhelming.

Hoglund's achievement (nicknamed the coffee grinder or peanut grinder) was not unique. The Tru-Coid required a pattern or template to form its trochoid shape. Gleason Works, a specialist machine tool manufacturer "with years of technical development of systems for the generation of geometric shapes," found another, less well-publicized solution—by controlling the operational cycle of the grinding machine closely enough to form the required shape. Other manufacturers were soon in the act; for the machines cost upward of $150,000 each and were needed, not just for production, but also for development work. GM bought three Tru-Coids before it had decided to produce the rotary, and Ford bought one even though it eventually decided not to go into rotary production.

How to apply the final chrome coat was an even more difficult problem to solve. The technique of electroplating, or depositing a thin film of metal in a bath with an electric current running through it, was well enough known, as were methods of honing the thin metal veneer. But the plating process was slow—taking up to fifteen hours. For the mass production of housings by traditional methods, said one observer, "GM would have electroplating baths strung out from New York to Los Angeles."

But by early 1972, help was on the way, although the method was not finally proved workable until late August 1972. A division of another well-known machinery manufacturer, Ex-Cell-O, devised a method of electroplating and honing the surface simultaneously. Hone-forming, as it was called, shortened the time required for plating from hours to a mere fifteen minutes, as well as reducing the amount of metal that had to be used. The slightly farcical secrecy that has always surrounded the GMRE development was illustrated once again when John De Lorean referred at a press conference in early September to a "fantastic breakthrough in production techniques" occurring within the past week. Dave Smith, the alert editor of *Ward's Auto World,* immediately guessed what this was and called up Ex-Cell-O. A spokesman there confirmed his guess, saying,

"You've got it then," as though everyone was playing a guessing game at a children's party.

There were other problems, of course. The side seals required grooves that had to be cut in the otherwise unremarkable side housing to an extraordinary degree of exactness; otherwise the seals would rock in their grooves and wear faster and more irregularly than they should. What is more, the slots had to stop exactly at the point where they met the pin which joined them to the apex seal —another tricky problem. But by the summer of 1972, both Gleason and the Hoglunds had come up with the answers, at a cost of something over $60,000 a machine. None of the other machinery required was as remarkable or as unique as the Tru-Coid or the Hone-Former, but it was different, and the many companies involved, Cross and Wilson, Gleason, and Ex-Cell-O, spent millions of dollars of their own money, partly because they saw a new market opening, and partly because Big Daddy GM asked them to help. They lived up to De Lorean's boast, and that summer Cole could safely assert that GM would produce a competitive rotary engine.

...*Mmmmmmmm*

"... a car with a name that sounds like a variety of light bulb,
that has the racy lines of a bathtub, and that is already more
expensive than U.S. subcompacts and many imports..."
                              —*Wall Street Journal*, October 1, 1971

Even if GM could design and produce a rotary-engined vehicle at
a reasonable price, there was, in 1970, very little likelihood that the
U.S. car buyer would be interested in such vehicles. Car buyers in
Europe, generally far readier to take to technical novelty than their
U.S. counterparts, had been thoroughly put off rotary-engined vehi-
cles by the well-publicized inadequacies of NSU's RO80.

The first rotary-engined car the U.S. driver was offered, the
Mazda, had all the disadvantages listed by the *Wall Street Journal*,
and more, and was being sold to them in a most haphazard fashion.
Yet within eighteen months it had become the "in" car. A magazine
as normally unimpressionable as *Fortune* could observe that the
rotary-engined "bathtub" made even Ferraris and Maseratis look
"suddenly conventional."

Yet Toyo Kogyo did not really have any idea of how to market
their vehicle in the United States. Their approach resembled a series
of commando raids rather than the carefully orchestrated invasion
plans laid by Toyota and Nissan. These two, the biggest Japanese
manufacturers, had established their bridgeheads in California,
where the Volkswagen had achieved its greatest impact, and which
always had the reputation of welcoming any automotive newcomer.
They had then moved on to the East Coast before mopping up the
great interior.

Toyo Kogyo, by constrast, simply shipped its cars from its own docks at Hiroshima to a few convenient U.S. ports and sold them nearby. For this reason, its first target was Seattle, Washington, a city never noted for its ready acceptance of anything new.

The first shipment of Mazdas arrived in May 1970. Shipments to Texas and Florida through the ports of Galveston and New Orleans followed. Nine months later, in the spring of 1971, Mazdas were first sold in California.

The companies marketing the cars—Mazda Northwest, Mazda Florida, etc.—were all independent of one another and reported directly to Hiroshima. Whichever proved to be the best sales force would be rewarded by being given more areas to exploit, either in the Midwest or on the eastern seaboard. In addition, the marketing executives took on dealers who sold other makes of car as well. In contrast to Volkswagen, and following the lead of other German manufactures, Toyota and Nissan insisted that their dealers sell only their cars.

Within eighteen months, this apparent recipe for failure had changed abruptly into dramatic success. Strangely enough, the Mazdas, first the R-100, then the RX-2, had rocketed into fourth place or better in any market where they were being sold. They had suddenly become the most fashionable vehicles in southern California. Thirty or more car dealers were vying for any new dealership. The excitement when a new showroom opened its doors was often so great that no cars could be sold at all because of the crush. Some dealers said they had not seen such enthusiasm for a new car since World War II. Others said they "hadn't seen crowds like this since they introduced the V-8." One comparison was more ominous. A California dealer was reminded of the enormous public interest when Ford introduced its ill-fated Edsel. "Unfortunately, people didn't buy the Edsel," he said, but quickly added, "On this car they are signing orders."

Despite a long dock strike on the West Coast, sales boomed; the demand was so great that at one dealership, allegedly, "every time a trailer brings in a new shipment, the salesmen run out and fight over who's going to get the cars."

This sudden public enthusiasm certainly did not include the car's shape. "It looks," wrote the *Detroit Free Press* about the RX-2, "like another of those boxy Japanese cars, which, by the way, is exactly what it is: a boxy Japanese car."

The New York Times agreed. "Unhappily, the Mazda is no

beauty," it noted. "Its unprepossessing outline is short and boxy, and the stylists have aggravated the shape by gussying it up with trim and ornaments."

The Japanese have a penchant for what they call "surface entertainment," and what Western taste would describe as overwrought and fussy decoration. Also, none of Toyo Kogyo's cars were designed purely to take the rotary engine. The Matsudas have never been able to afford the risk. So the R-100 and its successors were all basic family saloons which happened to be powered by rotary engines. By European standards, they were all somewhat cramped, and although road-holding was not bad, it was universally agreed the suspension was poor.

What is more—even the engine, the major reason for the car's success, was not perfect. A report noted the familiar Wankel problem of bucking "when lightly accelerating after rounding a low-speed corner."

"The one disappointment," noted the *Times*, "is the slow start. Pulling away from a traffic light or the curb, the rev counter winds up toward the big numbers, out of proportion to the numbers on the speedometer." But, the report added, "this does not last long. By the time 2,500 rpm or so is reached, the car is well on its way, because that is where the torque cranks in." From that point on in the experience of driving a Mazda, the superlatives started.

Car buffs wrote to their favorite magazines naming the large native vehicles they had overtaken at 110 miles per hour on the freeways. Others compared the level of noise—or rather, lack of it—at high speeds to those in the best of cars: In the $3,000 Mazda, as on the $25,000 Rolls-Royce, the loudest noise to be heard at seventy miles per hour was the ticking of a clock.

The Mazda rotary engine had two of the qualities most prized by American, and especially Californian, motorists. It was utterly smooth, however hard you pressed on the accelerator, and its performance did not diminish as you went faster. The rotary thrives at high revolutions, when ordinary engines sound strained. The *Wall Street Journal*, October 1, 1971, said that "the car accelerates fast enough to leave the tires hanging onto the wheels for dear life and the speedometer moves over the ninety mph mark without the driver noticing an increase in engine noise vibration."

Even *Consumer Reports*, issued by the Consumers Union, was as enthusiastic as it had ever been. Reporting on a 1971 RX-2, the *Reports* wrote:

[The] engine was impressively smooth and quiet at all speeds—especially when compared to the rough and raucous four-cylinder engines in most small imports . . . the Wankel was so smooth and quiet that we had to take care not to exceed 7,000 revolutions per minute, the maximum recommended engine speed . . . acceleration would have been creditable for a V-8 model . . . As small cars go the Mazda RX-2 is difficult to fault . . . Its ride comfort, especially on freeways, was above par for its class, and acceleration, handling, and braking were impressive regardless of class.

In addition, like most Japanese cars (and especially Mazdas), the R-100 and its successors were well finished with a great many small extras thrown in as part of the price of the standard model. More specialist magazines went overboard for the engine. In one often-quoted remark, *Car and Driver* said that the Mazda's acceleration "would suck the doors off any other small sedan." *Road Test* magazine ran features on the rotary almost every month. In the middle of 1972, it hired Karl Ludvigsen to do a monthly report on the whole rotary scene, ranging from the use of rotaries in airplanes to the complexities of the licensing situation. The Mazda itself was considered a worthy competitor for expensive European imports with well-deserved sporty reputations, like Alfa-Romeo or BMW.

"Is the Mazda RX-2, then, in the same league as the two Europeans?" asked *Road and Track*. "We have to say it is . . . it offers real enjoyment to the enthusiast at a price many enthusiasts can afford when the European machinery is prohibitive." The RX-2 was $1,000 cheaper than the Alfa and nearly $2,000 less than the BMW *Road and Track* was testing at the same time as the Mazda. This feeling of excitement generated by the RX-2 enabled Mazda to charge $450 over its usual price for the privilege of rotary motoring.

The appeal of successive Mazdas was summed up by their main booster and salesman, C. R. (Dick) Brown, who had been appointed general manager of Mazda Motors of America (MMA) in December 1970. "We stress that we have a small car that does not have the drawback of others: too little power. . . . Because of the ever-rising cost of automobiles, they are less and less of a status symbol. People today like to buy a small car, and we have something that draws their attention."

Brown had the right instincts and training to sell the Mazda rotaries. He had been toughened up by U.S. paratrooper service and working for Chrysler during a period of its roughest corporate in-fighting.

But he inherited a ramshackle structure. MMA had a headquarters at Compton, near Los Angeles, but no authority over the three other factory-owned distributorships in Seattle, Miami, and Houston. The company's president, Jiro Morihawa, was a liaison man with the factory rather than a territorial manager, and he and Brown only acquired an integrated operation in May 1973, after the Mazda boom had passed through its heroic, spectacular earliest growth.

But even with his limited authority as general manager, Brown's ideas were clear. He saw that this was his once-in-a-lifetime chance to make a name for himself in the auto industry and was determined not to muff it. He laid down the same guidelines for dealerships that had been so successful with VW, Toyota, and Nissan: no sharing of premises with other makes, adequate financing (reputedly at least $500,000 per showroom), and instead of the haphazard spread of dealers, a proper, if gradual, spread to new areas. During 1972, Brown hired two other experienced marketing men, Sid Fogel from Chrysler and Lou Glasgow from Buick, to take charge of organizing regions, Fogel in the Midwest, Glasgow on the eastern seaboard. Toward the end of the year, they launched the car with great showmanship. Glasgow staged a wingding starring Count Basie at the Plaza Hotel in New York in November. Fogel repeated the performance two days later at the Marriott Motor Hotel in Chicago. Before the end of the year, the Mazda had even conquered Detroit: It was the star of the November automobile show.

Initially, Glasgow and Fogel had an easy job. Both potential customers and dealers had been presold on the car, partly by the excitement emanating from the West Coast, but partly too from the advertisements. Brown had hired, as Mazda's advertising and sales promotion manager, Bill Power, an advertising executive he had worked with at Chrysler. Power and Mazda's advertising agency, Foote Cone and Belding, devised a series of advertisements that would make the rotary engine famous throughout the United States.

The first object of any Mazda advertisement was educational: to convey to the public just what was so different and superior about a rotary engine. (Like General Motors, Mazda did not refer to it as the Wankel. "Only this company—not Wankel," said Brown, "has developed this engine so that it can be produced at reasonable cost.")

Some anonymous genius in the agency devised a radio advertisement to show Californians that the Wankel went merely "mmmmmmmm" while other ordinary engines went "boing-boing." This was then translated into television terms with a youngster on a pogo stick bouncing up and down to symbolize the vibrant, old-fashioned nature of the reciprocating engine.

The resulting advertisements clicked with the right segment of the American public—if not necessarily the rich, the better educated. Again following in the wake of VW, the Mazda appealed to that large and receptive slice of the U.S. public with college educations, with incomes between $10,000 and $20,000 a year, and with a willingness to be slightly different. Study after study told the same story: that Mazda was taking sales from other Japanese imports, from sportier U.S.-built vehicles like the Mustang, and from foreign sports cars, like the much more expensive BMW and Alfa-Romeo.

The Mazda had another trump card. Even before the company started selling its cars in the United States, Yamamoto had learned how to cope with the U.S. limits for air pollution to be enforced in all cars sold in the United States by 1975.

REAPS (Rotary Engine Antipollution System) was a thermal reactor which relied on additional combustion rather than chemical reactions to remove the pollutants. The "reactor" was simply a foot-long cylinder, which mixed the rotary's hot exhaust gases with a stream of fresh air. The mixture ignited and converted the deadly carbon monoxide and the polluting hydrocarbons into harmless water and carbon dioxide. To reduce the amount of pollution from the engine itself, the ignition was retimed and the combustion chamber reshaped so that little gas was concentrated in its trailing part, the area where combustion was worst because of the flat, thin shape of the edges of a rotary chamber. A tiny computer was installed in each car to ensure that the right amounts of air were injected into the various parts of the system at the right time by opening and closing the eleven air control valves in the engine.

Mazda only needed a simpler version of this unit to meet the

1970 California antipollution requirements. But the potential for improvement was always there. In May 1972 Mazda announced it could meet the 1975 pollution levels in time, even though the U.S. motor industry (apart from GM) was clamoring for at least a year's delay in implementing the regulations. A year later, despite a stream of hostile comment from Henry Ford and his company about the validity of the tests involved, Mazda triumphantly passed the federal government tests carried out by the Environmental Protection Agency. "Concerned" car buyers could feel they were being environmentally responsible as well as fashionable in buying a Mazda.

Despite the severe shocks administered to car imports from Germany and Japan by the currency upheavals of late 1971 and 1972 that increased the value of the Deutsche mark and the yen, and new U.S. import taxes, the glamour of the Mazda kept the sales impetus going. Of all the car importers, only Mazda did not reduce sales targets for 1972. Brown could legitimately boast that Mazda was "the only car maker in the industry that did not use price as a selling point . . . we don't have a $2,000 car for instance." But the currency revolution did have one profound effect on the U.S. car industry. For the first time in a generation, it became possible to build a small car in the United States and sell it at a decent profit—a point not lost on Ford with its Pinto, nor on GM with its plans for a range of Vega subcompacts expanded to include rotary-engined models.

Customers were prepared to overlook the price of the Mazda (nearly $1,000 more than a VW Beetle, for instance) as new models were introduced. At the end of 1972, Mazda had introduced into California the RX-3 with an automatic transmission to answer the complaints about jerkiness and lack of acceleration at slow speeds.

Sales continued to rise impressively. In 1970, Mazda sold only 2,100 cars in the United States, of which a third were rotaries—a mere 649 cars. In 1971, 20,000 cars were sold, over half of which were rotaries. In 1972, the figure was 58,000, of which three-quarters—42,609 cars—were rotary engined. These sales had not been achieved by saturating the market with large numbers of outlets. At the beginning of 1973, Mazda had just over 300 dealers in the United States.

The parent company was euphoric. In 1972, for the first time in its forty-year history, Toyo Kogyo's sales rose above the $1 billion level. No wonder Brown and Matsuda dreamed aloud of selling

300,000 rotary-engined cars within a couple of years, of starting to build cars in the United States before the end of the decade, even of supplanting the eternally troubled American Motors as the fourth largest auto maker in the country. It did not, seemingly, matter that the profit margins were being eroded by the cost of building up a base in the United States, not to mention Toyo Kogyo's promise to replace engines where necessary. But no one at Mazda or in the Tokyo stock market—where Toyo Kogyo shares had soared with the Mazda boom from a low of 140 yen in 1971 to a peak of 589 in 1972—heeded the words of skeptics like Bob Kovacik, editor of *Sports Cars of the World:*

People can buy a car that will perform almost as well as the Mazda for a lot less money . . . Mazda will be successful the next couple of years by merchandising its cars to people who've long been interested in the Wankel engine, but what happens after that?

18

Wankel Fever and the Stock Market

"Here are four ways to make your corporation's stock bound up. 1. Rename your company 'The Wankel Works.' 2. Announce that you have just received a contract to make a screw that might be used in Wankel engines. 3. Announce that you have just hired three scientists to look into Wankel engine research. 4. Announce that the clerk in your shipping room has a brother-in-law who is thinking about buying a car that has a Wankel engine."
—*Wall Street Journal,* June 1972

The price of Toyo Kogyo's shares had started to move on the Tokyo Stock Exchange in 1971 as the ever-alert Japanese investment community grasped the implications of GM's license agreement and the increasing sales of Mazdas in the United States. By contrast, for over a year after the signature in Cole's office, there was barely any movement in the price of the common stock of Curtiss-Wright, the company which stood to gain most from the GM deal. Indeed, the most important rotary-related investment negotiations of the year took place completely outside the stock market when the Israeli-British Bank (IBB) tried to organize a syndicate to buy the rights to the rotary engine from Curtiss-Wright. By this time, the IBB was involved in several other Wankel deals: It had an option to buy a quarter of Wankel G.m.B.h.; it held large amounts of genusscheine; and Savkel, then its subsidiary, had just negotiated a license to make rotary engines in Israel.

For the Curtiss-Wright deal, the IBB needed allies. Martin

Rosen, a former senior official at the World Bank, and Lee M. Elman, a deal finder, brought in Model Roland, a leading Wall Street brokerage house. At one point they even interested the legendary investment banker Charlie Allen, who had made untold millions out of Syntex, the first successful contraceptive pill. But somehow the deal was never made—though no one connected with it can explain exactly why. It was largely a question of mood. In the cold and uncertain climate that surrounded the dollar in 1971, foreign investors held back, and prospective American ones seemed to feel that Curtiss-Wright's directors might change their minds. Although they appeared eager to sell their rights to the engine even after the GM license agreement had been signed, there remained a lurking fear that Curtiss-Wright would increase its price or refuse to deal at all. Within Model Roland there was also opposition; its motor analyst, Don Peterson, was never very bullish on the engine. He was particularly worried about the fuel consumption problem.

The first native American Wankel stock enthusiast was Bob Birr, an investment analyst and stock salesman who moved to the San Francisco offices of a leading broker, W. E. Hutton, early in 1971. Birr was and is an auto buff, and his interest had been stimulated by the early rumors that GM might take a license and by a rather inaccurate report prepared in Jerusalem for Goodbody, his former employer, that dealt with IBB's heavy involvement in the engine and the license Savkel acquired in 1969. He got as much information as he could from Curtiss-Wright. One of the press clippings mentioned David Cole, a "skeptic turned believer" as far as the engine was concerned. Birr telephoned Cole, who told him that the rotary-engined Mazda was being sold on the West Coast. Cole impressed Birr as "not just the son of the president of General Motors but as a man with a mind of his own." And, early in 1971, Birr persuaded his employers to hire Cole as a consultant.

By the summer of 1971, Birr was recommending Curtiss-Wright stock to anyone who would listen, which did not include many mutual fund men. When trying to sell to one particular fund when Curtiss-Wright was in the $10-$20 range, Birr pointed to the income almost sure to come from the GM deal alone. But Curtiss-Wright's poor reputation was enough to put off serious purchasers. "It won't make any difference," they said. "The management will throw away any earnings they make."

When Curtiss-Wright had moved to $17, David Cole talked to

the fund's managers, with equally negative results. With the stock at $28 and again at $30, they ignored Birr's further urgings. When the stock had reached $40, they asked him whether they should buy, and they eventually did at $42–$45, to make a small profit.

By mid-1971, the rotary-engined Mazda was beginning its climb to fame. But, as is so often the case, the New York financial community completely ignored what was happening on the West Coast. The first sign of the Wankel spring that was to come was at, of all unlikely spots, one of the regular meetings of the Machinery Analysts' group of the New York Society of Investment Analysts, in August 1971. Howard Carver, the chairman of the Gleason Works, was giving one of his regular six-monthly talks to the group and demonstrating some of the machinery his company was working on. This included drawings of the trochoid grinder Gleason had under development to compete with Tri-Ordinate's machine, itself still a secret confined to the Hoglunds and GM's Hydra-Matic Division. Gleason's work caught the attention of Hutton's machinery analyst, George Ulrich, and that fall he and Birr started work on the investment possibilities of the Wankel, not just in terms of Curtiss-Wright stock, but any other that might be involved.

One problem that soon came up was the virtual absence of suitable stocks to invest in. There was Curtiss-Wright, and there were a handful of machinery stocks, like Gleason and Ex-Cell-O. But many of the companies most deeply affected, like Tri-Ordinate, were privately held, and others, like GM itself, were simply too big for the Wankel story to be a significant element in their earnings' makeup. To confuse matters further, many of the equipment manufacturers stood to lose almost as much from the possible replacement of the orthodox engine by the Wankel as they were likely to gain from its adoption. In one report, for instance, Ulrich showed that if GM adopted the particular type of front-wheel-drive layout he thought they would, Gleason stood to lose more from the loss of orders on its basic lines of complicated bevel-gear cutters as it did to gain from supplying machinery to grind rotary trochoids and cut rotary side seals.

Undaunted, Pattison of Model Roland, as chairman of the Machinery Analysts' group, arranged a special meeting on January 6, 1972, which gave birth to the Wankel boom. Even before the meeting, the Curtiss-Wright stock had started to move. Stirred by a private meeting of institutional investors in Hutton's office before the analysts' gathering, it rose from thirteen to eighteen that same day.

The meeting was crammed with up to 350 eager listeners, prepared to believe in the market's next big "play." Wankel fever proved contagious, and the meeting inaugurated "six or eight beautiful months." The missionaries that day who spread the Wankel gospel so successfully included Cole, Carver, Jan Norbye, a Norwegian-born automotive journalist and author of the standard work on the engine, and Bob Brooks, another founder member of the Wankel Club.

Brooks, an amiable management and marketing consultant, lives, by coincidence, in Waukegan, Illinois, a few streets away from the headquarters of Outboard Marine, the pioneer producers of Wankel engines in the United States. He operates out of a basement study which is scattered with parts of various Wankel engines and fouled-up valves from reciprocating engines to show the effect on them of pollution-control devices. Working partly for Hutton and other brokers, and mostly for himself, Brooks has been the Wankel's most tireless propagandist in the United States, ever ready with a quote for the inquiring journalist, always pumping out stories to point to new opportunities, new excitements to come in the wonderful world of the Wankel.

The basic text of the boom was an extremely sober analysis of the situation issued by Ulrich three days before. Although Ulrich was very cautious, almost academic in his approach, the title "The Wankel Engine—Revolution in Auto Design" was enough for many investors. Over the next few months, Ulrich, Brooks, and Cole spread the glad tidings throughout the United States, Cole's presence emphasizing how deeply his father, and thus GM, were involved in the engine.

By the middle of February, the boom had really taken off, to the dismay of some conservative participants. Some investors were so confused about Curtiss-Wright's exact arrangements with GM that they thought GM would be paying a royalty on each engine it produced.

On February 17, the president of Ex-Cell-O, one of the stocks caught up in the boom, tried to inject some realism into the situation. "Based on what I know about the Wankel engine, the speculative fever is overdone," he said. "We see nothing indicating that there will be any release of orders for machine tools for the Wankel engine. And I don't think there's any assurance that the Wankel engine will be the engine of the future."

As so often happens with such statements, it had only a temporary effect. Curtiss-Wright stock, which had run up to thirty-two/thirty-three, met with some profit taking. Over a million shares were sold by one source alone, supposed to be the IBB, which had so cannily bought heavily at a third of the current price the previous year. To cool the fever, the Stock Exchange banned credit purchases of the stock, as it does whenever it feels the market in a particular stock is out of control. But the turnover remained enormous, the price never went below twenty-five and, at the end of April, resumed its upward climb, fueled by reports that GM would be in production within eighteen months.

In the spring of 1972, the market in any of the stocks involved was, to put it mildly, touchy. The day before the Gleason Works was due to issue some new common stock to its existing stockholders, Nils Hoglund's Tri-Ordinate Corporation announced the GM had ordered more of its "peanut grinders." This news that Gleason's great rival seemed to be capturing more than its fair share of the Wankel machinery business "sent Gleason stock into a tailspin," Ulrich recalls, and "damn near destroyed the Gleason secondary [stock issue]." But it sent another stock soaring: Digital Equipment, the electronics company which makes the small computer that controlled the Tri-Ordinate machine.

By this time, GM was desperately worried about possible lawsuits or action by the Securities and Exchange Commission. Four years previously, there had been an enormous fuss, followed by legal action, over the misuse of confidential information by directors and executives of Texas Gulf Sulphur, a mining company. Since then this sort of "insider" trading had become the object of suspicious scrutiny by the government. GM issued a learned document to its staff on "potential legal problems related to disclosures incident to rotary development."

This was not as stern in tone as the warning it was to issue later that year and started with what must have been one of the understatements of 1972: "Speculation as to possible early production by GM of automobiles powered by the rotary engine undoubtedly has been a factor in the fluctuations in the price of Curtiss-Wright stock recently." As a consequence of the Texas Gulf Sulphur case, "a GM executive or employee with material inside information as to the potentialities and development status of the rotary could conceivably be regarded as an insider of Curtiss. . . . The law places the corporation and all insiders in vulnerable positions."

By June, in a generally dull market, the Wankel was "the only play in town." Brooks was quoted as saying he "believed that the U.S. auto industry would have turned over almost completely to Wankels by 1980 and that the economic impact of the engine would eventually dwarf such major postwar technological developments as xerography, Edwin Land's Polaroid camera, and color television."

Curtiss-Wright stock was climbing fast through the 1940s, and any other stock with the remotest connection with the engine was caught up in the tail of the comet. Stocks like Gleason's and the Cross Company's, a major producer of engine assembly lines, had doubled in price during a half year in which most machine tool stocks had performed drearily or worse.

Ralph Cross had stated that his company was bidding on most of the major components for the Wankel for three or four companies, including two of the Big Three, though none had actually appropriated any money for tooling for the Wankel. But his reasoning was impressive; he reckoned that the Wankel would have the same effect on the U.S. machine tool industry as it had seen in the 1950s when engine design had last changed radically.

"It took us about ten years to retool the industry for the Kettering engine . . . we don't think it would take anything less than a like amount of time for the Wankel."

This provided a solid enough basis for some form of rise in the stocks most directly involved, but much of the market activity was less logical. For instance, one broker was recommending the shares of Brunswick Corporation, the second largest manufacturer of outboard engines, because it had just taken out a license to produce Wankels, a license Outboard Marine, the biggest in the field, had had for six years.

And there was a new play in town, American-Israeli Paper (AIP), which made its money out of producing paper (itself a most unglamorous business at the time) in Israel (always a high risk area). But at the time it owned half the stock of Savkel (see page 149), which the year before had taken out a license and was cooperating with Curtiss-Wright to produce a range of small rotary industrial engines in Israel. AIP's stock duly trebled in price even though the company's chairman, Joseph Mazer, went out of his way to damp down expectations, pointing out that they were "talking about a complete unknown. . . . Savkel hasn't even produced the first prototype and who knows about the costs or the selling price?"

By that time the boom was worrying many early Wankel backers. Bob Birr, for instance, was amazed by the rise in AIP. "I never believed," he said, "that Wall Street could get that excited about a purely drawing board transaction."

The warning signs took two forms: The major stocks involved in the boom had risen too fast, and even more dangerously, there were other companies even more remotely concerned with the engine than AIP that had also soared in price.

As one experienced analyst put it, "This happens time and again as investors grasp an attractive concept and then start groping to find peripheral companies whose stock prices haven't advanced along with those of the industry leaders."

With the Wankel the fringe got really way out. The stock of the little-known Mite Corporation nearly doubled in a week, merely because its annual report mentioned that the company was supplying components for some of the machine tools GM was using to produce the engine. More comical and serious was the story of the Heinicke Corporation, a small manufacturer of medical cleansing equipment. Late one Thursday in the middle of June, it issued a three-line press release saying that it had bought American International Trade, Inc., a Seattle company which "has a contract with Curtiss-Wright Corporation to purchase the Wankel rotary combustion engine for marine and industrial applications." On the Friday morning, Heinicke stock soared from $3 to $7.125, adding over $5 million to the value of the company. At lunch time the American Stock Exchange suspended trading. Heinicke then issued a lengthy explanatory statement, which spelled out that American International Trade was worth at most $100,000, that Heinicke could not afford to buy many engines, and that any it did acquire (to be imported from Toyo Kogyo) would require "extensive testing" before they could be used for marine purposes.

To professional investors such farcical episodes were reliable indications of a boom about to fade, a balloon about to burst; at the first signal they would desert this particular fashion. Within a few weeks, an excuse was found. On July 5, Alan G. Loofbourrow, Chrysler's vice-president in charge of engineering, told Bob Irvin of the *Detroit News* that "the Wankel rotary engine will turn out to be the most unbelievable fantasy ever to hit the world of auto industry." Its chief, indeed its only, attraction was its novelty, and "the U.S. car driver is a pretty astute individual . . . novelty is not enough," and gave the unpromising results of Chrysler's own analysis of the Wankel's problems.

Loofbourrow's views were well known in Detroit and had been quoted in the local press a couple of months previously without any major effect on the market. But Irvin, as well as being the *News*'s "amusement editor," was also the Detroit stringer for Reuter's financial news tape, and within a few minutes the story was all over the country. It provided an excellent excuse for a great sell-off.

For two days Curtiss-Wright stock, which had been trading at over fifty, did not open. When a syndicate of interested brokers could be found to try and buy up the masses of stock on offer, Curtiss-Wright opened again—at thirty-six. The damage was horrendous. There was, said one trader, "blood all over the street."

At the same time that Curtiss-Wright reopened, Hutton issued another report, also written by George Ulrich, on the investment implications of the Wankel. This was a follow-up to the research that had sparked off the boom six profitable months before. It was decidedly more cautious in tone than his earlier study, partly as a reaction to the soaring stock prices.

He warned his readers to avoid the highly speculative stocks within the "Wankel group . . . where only limited information is available," and to concentrate on those few machine tool stocks that were still selling on unremarkable earning's multiples despite their rise. But even among machinery manufacturers, he advised a partial profit-taking in Gleason Works, which had risen by two-thirds in the first half of the year. By then Curtiss-Wright, also a "sell" recommendation, had bounced back to fifty-two. At that price it was selling at eighty-seven times its estimated earnings for 1972—the sort of valuation which assumed, against any real evidence, that the company's profits would more than double and then continue to soar for years. Ulrich's caution was echoed by other brokers close to the action.

But by then it was "a traders' not an analysts' market," and the fundamentals of the situation had been forgotten—for a short time anyway. Spirits quickly recovered, and within a few weeks the stock was at an all-time high of 59 5/8–7/8. One brokerage house took on 10,000 shares to add to the 5,000 it already held, in the firm conviction—encouraged by the floor specialist's apparent attitude—that next morning the stock would open above the magical sixty barrier it had previously approached, but never actually broken. In the absence of the Curtiss-Wright chief trader, the rest of the firm's representatives went off to Wall Street's then favorite watering hole, Oscar's, for a celebratory drink. But they were wrong; once the sixty mark was broken, masses of stock were offered for sale. Curtiss-Wright never did hold at sixty.

Since those halcyon summer days, all (or almost all) of stock market interest in the Wankel has been anticlimax. Wall Street moved on to other plays, and not even Gerstenberg's announcement in late August 1972 that GM would produce a rotary-engined car stoked the fires again. There were occasional flurries. Curtiss-Wright stock jumped forty percent six months later, in March 1973, when American Motors announced that it, too, had taken out a license—to make it, once again, the Exchange's star mover. Even American-Israeli Paper stirred in its sleep. But since then Curtiss-Wright has returned to the depths of the teens whence it sprang.

Yet the rotary dream was not altogether dead. In December 1972, a previously unknown company, the Aadan Corporation, which claimed to own land in Nicaragua worth $3.6 million, announced that it had acquired the rights to the Hinckley-Beloit-Hornbostel rotary engine. This was the result of forty years' development by John N. Hinckley, an instructor at the small Wisconsin college of Beloit. Within a few weeks, the price of Aadan's stock had nearly doubled. The following March, the Securities and Exchange Commission (SEC) finally got around to stopping any deals in Aadan's stock. Only then did the SEC discover such relevant facts as the purchase price for Aadan's Nicaraguan lands—$26,000—and issued a warrant for the arrest on fraud charges of Mr. Fred Franklin, Aadan's financial vice-president. Mr. Hinckley is still looking for a backer, and the last news was that the SEC was still (fruitlessly) searching for Mr. Franklin.

19

Henry Ford and Other Latecomers

"Well, GM is going into it heavily, and we don't want to be left at the starting gate."

—HENRY FORD II

Henry Ford could, as usual, afford to be blunter than anyone else in the auto industry. He had blurted out the generally unspoken thoughts of many other auto industry executives. Where GM had led, others—makers of motorcycles as well as cars—would follow. A mere five hours after Ed Cole had signed the license for GM, Henn and Hutzenlaub were on their way to Japan, where Nissan, the country's second biggest motor company, had just bought a license. In the next couple of years, Toyota would follow suit, along with Suzuki, Yamaha, and Yamasaki, three of the world's biggest manufacturers of motorcycles.

But the strongest pressure after the license purchase by GM was not on the Japanese but on Ford, which saw its hard-won position as the auto industry's pace-setter threatened by GM's unexpectedly adventurous behavior over the rotary. As always, the attitude of Ford the company toward the engine was colored by the feeling of Henry Ford the man.

Ford is a unique phenomenon in modern industry. His prejudices, his likes and dislikes are still the unquestioned law in his company. Any new car requires his personal approval; and why not? Won't it bear his name?

At twenty-eight years of age, Ford wrested control of the company from his aging grandfather and his henchmen. Today, nearly thirty years later, long after the executives who rebuilt his company have left, to be replaced by men he appointed, his prejudices are that much more difficult to buck. And Ford apparently has never liked the Wankel, or was it that he never heard the arguments in its favor?

Nevertheless, his company has never been one to close any options. It protected itself from the Wankel threat in an intelligent if, to the outsider, confusing way. Ford concluded it might need rotary engines in a hurry to arm its precious Mustang to compete with a possible sporty rotary-engined Vega; otherwise, and for the first time since the Mustang's introduction in 1964, Ford would lose the initiative in the "swinger's" market. In the longer term it needed to be able to produce its own design of Wankel.

In theory, Ford could buy rotary engines from Comotor, but this was not a practical possibility. Comotor's program was well behind schedule, and it had no real hope of providing engines in any quantity before 1974, if then. A more promising approach was to do a deal with Toyo Kogyo, either through buying ready-made engines, or buying enough shares in the company to be able to treat it as an in-house engine supplier, with the additional advantage of buying into an unequaled ready-made source of patents, know-how, and technical personnel.

Each company were dominated by one man—Ford by Henry Ford, Toyo Kogyo by Kohei Matsuda—and at first they found it relatively easy to get on. They had been in touch about pollution research since 1968. In 1969, Ford, Toyo Kogyo, and Nissan formed a joint company, JATCO, to produce automatic transmissions to a Ford design in Japan.

For the next two years, until the talks finally broke down in March 1972, Ford tried hard to buy up to a quarter of Toyo Kogyo. This was very much in line with the policy of U.S. motor companies toward the Japanese, whom they greatly admired and from whose market they had been so long excluded. It was a mark of the changed balance of power in the automotive world that the American company was prepared to take a minority interest; a few years before, it would have demanded 100 percent control. Japanese attitudes had also changed. At the end of the 1960s, as sales of Japanese cars to the United States mounted, there were real fears of reprisals if the Japanese market remained closed to foreigners. At the same time, a number of the smaller Japanese motor companies, vulnerable to the competitive pace set by the two biggest, Toyota and Nissan, seemed even to the intensely nationalistic Japanese government to be useful victims whose sacrifice would prevent any general retaliation against Japanese motor exports. So Chrysler was allowed to buy a third of the car division of the mighty Mitsubishi group, and GM picked up a similar stake in Isuzu.

However, Toyo Kogyo proved a different matter. Talks went on all through 1971 with varying prospects. At times agreement seemed near; then, seemingly, the talks broke down. Yet when Will Scott, Ford's chief negotiator, went over to wind up the discussions that summer, he apparently found the way clearer than he thought. Their final breakdown in March 1972 was for two reasons.

Ford had not fully anticipated the currency realignment of late 1971 and, therefore, had not bought enough yen to pay for its proposed stake in Toyo Kogyo. Once the yen's value had bounced up at the end of the year, Ford found that the dollar cost of its investment had risen by nearly a fifth. More fundamental on Matsuda's part was simple pride, nationalism reinforced by the natural dislike of takeover, of a family whose proudly independent company had survived and prospered against the odds. Ford's proposed stake of twenty-five percent was, said Matsuda, tantamount to being taken over by Ford from the legal point of view. What is more—the American company "wanted a degree of participation in management."

Matsuda's final offer would have given Ford a quarter of Toyo Kogyo's business, *excluding the rotary engine business*. In other words, said one disgusted Ford man, "a quarter of exactly nothing," since Ford's prime interest in acquiring a stake in Toyo Kogyo was as a source of supply of the rotary engine. The result was that Ford "was left at the altar."

But the breakdown of the talks did not mean the end of the relationship. In the summer of 1972, Ford thought of importing and marketing small rotary-engined Mazda pickup trucks to compete with the Toyotas and Datsuns which were proving so successful in the U.S. market. And Ford tried to secure a regular supply of rotary engines—allegedly at a rate of 10,000 a month—from Toyo Kogyo.

The other side of Ford's strategy, the long-term development of its own rotary power plant, was also sensible if inconclusive. After selling GM a license, NSU-Wankel/Curtiss-Wright were able to impose stiffer terms on other U.S. motor companies. In July 1971, the *Wall Street Journal* reported from Frankfurt that Ford and the German licensees were near agreement on a license that would commit Ford to an entrance fee of $10 million and royalties of between three-and-a-half and five percent on every Wankel sold. In November, a year after GM, Ford signed up for its license.

The public announcement made it appear far more limited than GM's deal. For one thing, it was merely between Audi-NSU and Ford-Werke, its German subsidiary, and therefore did not cover the United States where Ford would still need Curtiss-Wright's permission to sell even German-made cars. In the words of the responsible Ford executive, the deal was "meant primarily to assist Ford in keeping abreast of technical developments in the rotary engine field and in relation to the proposed equity investment by Ford in Toyo Kogyo." The terms were a $2.3 million entrance fee to the Wankel Club and agreement to a royalty on each rotary engine made in Germany.

But the agreement also contained a secret, and more far-reaching, option clause. Ford acquired the right to take out a full license covering the whole world at any time before November 1973. The cost would be a maximum of $55 million, of which up to $20 million would go to Curtiss-Wright and the rest (minus the payment already made by Ford-Werke) to NSU-Wankel. The conditions of payment were complicated. The money would either be paid as option fees, similar to those paid by GM, or on more favorable terms, as a form of royalty as production of rotary-engined vehicles was stepped up.

The license had a number of advantages from Ford's point of view. At minimum cost, it was keeping its options open and getting access to the requisite know-how. But it did not have to reveal the full conditions of the license in public, and because the agreement had been made primarily with NSU, Ford and Lee Iacocca, his number-two man, could blandly deny that there had been any contact or discussion of a license with Curtiss-Wright, thus leading reporters to assume that Ford did not have the right to make or sell a rotary-engined vehicle in the United States.

Ford's approach to actually making the engine work was also very different from GM, or indeed from most of the other licensees. It was not too proud to learn and build on what had been done elsewhere. Like GM, it started with Mazda engines, gradually changing them until they became more truly Ford designed; unlike GM, it did not try any radical novelties. It even modeled one design on NSU's work—closely enough even to call it the KKM 210; GM was always too proud to learn from what one executive in an exuberant moment called "those dumb Europeans."

Although Ford spent only a tenth of GM's annual $40 million in development costs, its efforts were successful enough to make the KKM 210 one of the very few rotary engines whose fuel consumption at low speeds compared favorably with reciprocating units. In the summer of 1972, it was forced to admit that some of Detroit's larger tool and die shops (those favorite hunting grounds of nosy reporters) had blueprints of a possible production rotary engine, though Ford said that this amounted to no more than an "investigation" of production possibilities. Even when Wankel fever was at its height, it was suspected that Henry Ford was not taking in the full positive story, but only the rotary's drawbacks.

Ford went out of its way to downgrade the rotary's status by publicizing other alternatives to the reciprocating engine. It stepped up its work on the gas turbine, and in August 1972 it bought an exclusive license to an even more revolutionary unit, the Stirling engine.

This was dreamed up by a Scottish clergyman in the early nineteenth century and had been partially developed by Philips, the enormous Dutch electrical company. Like the engine used in steam locomotives, it was an "external combustion" engine, where combustion heat caused motion in a different chamber, not—as with the Wankel or a reciprocating engine—in the one where combustion had taken place. An earlier version of the Stirling had been examined in depth by General Motors, but turned down a decade before. Despite some theoretical advantages in emission standards and fuel economy, it was strictly a long-term venture. Nevertheless, together with the turbine and the Wankel, it was listed by Ford as an alternative power unit.

Ford's attitude was conditioned by the need to show the public that it was not caught out by GM's initiative and to show the government that it was not neglecting any opportunity to improve combustion processes. But the other two U.S. motor manufacturers could afford to have altogether simpler attitudes. Chrysler was against the Wankel; American Motors was for it.

Chrysler's hostility had been expressed in Loofbourrow's denunciation which had so upset Wall Street. On the other hand, Chrysler freely admitted that it had been talking to Curtiss-Wright about a possible license; it had been keeping a close watch on rotary developments and even had a modest development program. But even at the height of the Wankel boom in the summer of 1972, it was far more openly negative in its attitude than anyone else in or around the American motor industry. Its reasons were the rotary's "inherent thermal inefficiency" and all the other doubts raised by experience with the Mazdas. And Chrysler raised one fundamental problem which has plagued the industry ever since: "If you put a Wankel on the market, it would sell like hot cakes . . . the big question is this: Will buyers come back for a second Wankel-powered car? We won't know that for a while."

As the pioneer manufacturer of compact and subcompact cars, American Motors (AMC) was naturally attracted by an engine which was boosted, however inaccurately, as especially suitable for smaller vehicles. At first AMC was primarily interested in buying some of GM's rotaries. But all through 1972, it was negotiating with the licensers to be able to make its own rotary engines.

But it was in Japan that Wankel fever had the greatest effect. Toyo Kogyo's bold policy was not really characteristic of Japanese companies as a whole. Toyota and Nissan behaved more typically. They imitated; they preferred to build on the pioneering efforts of others.

Nissan had already taken out a license earlier in 1970 and was already emerging as a force to be reckoned with in the rotary world—judging by the number and importance of the patents taken out by Nissan's engineers. Its efforts were partly simply to catch up, for, by the terms of its license, it was excluded from learning of Toyo Kogyo's developments, a clause inspired by Toyo Kogyo's fear that otherwise its much larger rival would quickly overtake it.

During 1972, Nissan's plans became clear. The company unveiled a prototype rotary engine at the Tokyo Motor Show that fall. It had peripheral ports; its seals were different from Toyo Kogyo's; and its engines incorporated some element of "stratified charging," but like the Mazda, it had twin rotors with two spark plugs each. Nissan apparently planned to start producing a sports car based on its small Sunny sedan in early 1974, only four years after taking out a license. Production would be 3,000 a month to start with, rising to 10,000 a month—a level it had taken Toyo Kogyo six years of production and six more years of research to reach. Nissan, the late-comer, naturally was able to build on others' efforts and speed up the timetable. What is more Nissan's license had been considerably broadened that year.

Originally, the companys license was limited to the production of automotive engines in Japan, between 80 and 100 bhp. The 1972 revision widened the permissible range of horsepower from 30 to 230, which covered any motor vehicle Nissan was ever likely to make. It brought marine engines into the agreement, and it allowed Nissan to make its engines anywhere in the world. This agreement cost several million dollars and was a further indication that Nissan was really serious about the rotary engine.

So, it seemed, was Toyota, the biggest of them all. Toyota had taken out a license covering most foreseeable motor uses in 1971 (it was later extended to cover Toyota's jeep-type vehicle as well), but the company clearly did not want to invest too much in the engine. It preferred to rely on Toyo Kogyo for its engines, possibly counting on its long-rumored plans to buy up Toyo Kogyo to enable Toyota to succeed where Ford had failed—and control a completely tied source of supply.

Until that happened, Toyota had to deal with Toyo Kogyo, and this was easier said than done. Before they could make any sort of arrangement, one legal difficulty had to be overcome. By the terms of its license, Toyo Kogyo was not entitled to sell engines separately. The discussions with NSU-Wankel in 1970 to widen the license broke down, and international arbitration was called for. But terms giving Toyo Kogyo "conditional freedom" to sell the engines separately were not agreed upon until 1972.

Even when that problem was out of the way, it became clear that Toyota's original idea of buying engines to put into cars to compete directly with the Mazda RX-2s and RX-3s was not acceptable. Kohei Matsuda was prepared only to sell engines for cars like Toyota's big Crown sedan, which were not going to compete with anything Toyo Kogyo might produce in the foreseeable future. Honeyed words like "Let's promote Japan's rotarization hand in hand" were not enough to produce a real deal. Toyota first agreed to buy rotary engines for use only in the Crown, but then backed down because "of differences in pricing and engine performance," instead speeding up its own rotary development program.

The motorcycle world, dominated anyway by the Germans and

Japanese, showed perhaps the most complete shift from indifference to enthusiasm over the rotary between 1970 and 1972. In a way the previous neglect was less comprehensible than the sudden enthusiasm. For motorcycles need engines which, like the Wankel, are inherently quiet and light. The first experimental batches of motorcycles appeared, in fact, during 1972, the Wankel's annus mirabilis. During the summer, Fichtel and Sachs installed one of its engines in a new bike made by its Hercules subsidiary, and later that year Yamaha proudly showed off at the Tokyo Motor Show a big new bike powered by a rotary made by Yanmar Diesel. It thus beat to the punch (if not to the market) its great rival Suzuki, which had taken out a license in November 1970, eighteen months before Yamaha. Both publicly expressed the aim of producing rotary-engined machines in significant numbers during 1974.

Suzuki's reasoning was straightforward. It had specialized in two-stroke engines and, rather than compete in the crowded four-stroke market, it opted for the rotary. Besides, Suzuki could foresee future air pollution and noise restrictions on motorcycles which the rotary, with its special noise "quality," a purr rather than a roar, could help solve.

Yamaha's ideas were more vague. It "felt the customers needed something new," and of course there were air pollution restrictions looming up, especially in the United States. Besides, Yamaha liked to "think of themselves as leaders in the field," and so were not going to be upstaged by their great rival Suzuki.

Yamaha has another problem. It is not allowed to sell rotary-engined machines to Britain and Europe, presumably because in the eighteen months between the Suzuki license and its own, a third motorcycle company, Britain's troubled BSA, had taken out its own license. Not to be left out of the act, another Japanese motorcycle company, Yamasaki, also took out a license in late 1972, but the great Soichiro Honda, the most famous of them all, was ostentatiously ignoring the whole rotary phenomenon. And within a year his ideas were to put a wrench in the whole rotary works.

20

The Rotary Honeymoon—GM Takes the Plunge

"... the rotary is in a position analogous to that of the jet aircraft engine in the late 1950s, with advantages in performance and cost that make it all but irresistible."

—*Fortune* magazine, July 1972

By the summer of 1972, even the most conservative board of directors could feel that in plumping for the rotary they were right in the middle of fashion. In Wall Street, as on the California freeways or the boardrooms of conservative manufacturing companies, the talk was all Wankel, and money was being put into the genusscheine, into Wankel Gm.B.h., into Wankel licenses, Wankel stocks, Wankel-powered cars, dealerships in which to sell the cars, machinery on which to produce the engines, books on the rotary, even into the plastic models of the engine which sold by the hundreds of thousands.

By the middle of August, rumors were flying that GM was about to make the crucial decision to produce a Wankel-engined Vega. Wall Street was in a tizzy, and one West Coast supplier kept asking journalists "if GM had made any official announcement yet."

As so often, the rumors were right. After a regular GM board meeting, held on August 28, a week earlier than usual because of the Labor Day weekend, a brief four-paragraph announcement was

made, cryptic enough not to upset GM watchers—for the sport of
GM watching would have been ruined if the prey had suddenly
become too open or garrulous. The crucial passage said:

Engine development and manufacturing processing work will continue and
if this progresses as anticipated, public introduction of the engine as an
option on the Vega line may be made in about two years. . . . Engineering
and development work on the rotary engine has proceeded to the point
where a commitment will be made for limited manufacturing facilities and
tools. . . .

Cynics could point to the let-out clauses and the judicious use of
the qualifying word "may." They could add that the announcement
was merely a rationalization of what Cole and his team had been
doing anyway. Nevertheless, the announcement was an historic one;
for the first time in its sixty-four-year history, the world's largest
automobile manufacturer was to offer for sale to the public cars
powered by something other than a piston engine.

Even the cynics were impressed that development work had
been shifted from GM's engineering laboratories to Chevrolet, the
division then designated to produce the car, though Hydra-Matic
was to produce the engines. The next news came from Chevrolet
itself at a press conference a few days later. John Z. De Lorean, who
was about to be promoted from Chevrolet boss to head of GM's car
and truck group, stated firmly that "GM does not experiment on the
public."

GM would ensure that everything was right with a rotary before
letting it out on the public, De Lorean went on, and the rightness had
to include fuel consumption. "I think," he said, "that it is very
probable that we would wind up with comparable fuel economy
once we get to the standards we have to have." Some observers took
these assurances with a pinch of salt: GM had made similar noises
when it had introduced the Vega, which then turned out to have the
same sort of problems of reliability and safety as the Corvair.

By the fall, the setting up of production machinery was in full
swing, and by the end of the year GM had, seemingly, stopped all
forward planning and development work on new piston engines. It
appeared to be the victim of the same single-minded devotion to the
rotary which had led to such trouble for Mercedes a few years

earlier. But it was clear that 1972 had been the rotary's year. By going ahead with it, slow, cautious GM had for once apparently stolen a march on its U.S. competitors. No one took any notice of Robert Templin, actually in charge of the GM rotary program, who muttered to a friendly journalist in September, "I hope I'm doing as well as everyone says I am."

If GM, the biggest of the U.S. auto manufacturers, would be the first to introduce a domestic rotary-engined car, American Motors, the smallest, was clearly not going to be far behind. In February 1973, after a year's negotiations, AMC announced a license agreement (described as a "very Scotch deal"), which closely resembled a scaled-down version of Ford's still secret option clause. AMC paid an initial royalty of $1.5 million spread over four years, with the first $350,000 paid on signing. AMC then had to pay a royalty on any engines produced, or, alternatively, a minimum payment, starting at $50,000 a year in 1976 and continuing until 1987. AMC, like Ford, limited its commitment by a cutoff clause. The maximum payment was $20 million, however many engines it produced. Furthermore, AMC could terminate the agreement at any time after the basic $1.5 million had been paid.

For its money the company got a comparatively narrow license —to make engines of between 80 and 200 bhp for passenger cars and jeeps in the United States, Canada, and Mexico. But since this covered virtually all AMC's car markets and its existing range of engines, it was perfectly adequate for the company's purposes.

AMC's attitude was refreshingly simple and, uniquely for Detroit, completely open—the company even allowed reporters to drive around in one of AMC's Gremlin cars with a rotary in it. Its policy, too, was quite clear: Until the company was selling 100,000 rotary-engined vehicles a year, it would try to buy its engines from GM—the Comotor unit was too expensive. Then it would start to build its own, which it would install in a new subcompact due out for the 1976 model year.

The openness and modesty of AMC's plans formed a sharp contrast with the confused noises coming out of GM. But through the mists it became obvious that the enthusiasm for the engine had spread and was no longer confined to Cole's own supporters within GM—though it still had its doubters within the corporation, as it has always had with any company that took it up. But by the end of

March, even the cautious Gerstenberg was saying that development was speeding up, noting how Cole had on his desk a little sign showing the number of days before the Wankel was due to be introduced.

By then other GM executives were publicly enthusing about the engine. Marketing men said the rotary would "produce the flexibility in design that will be necessary to produce a small car without sacrificing passenger space."

Bill Mitchell, GM's top stylist, agreed: "This means a lower hood, a lighter car, more room inside. We've had them in Chevrolets. You had to look at the instruments to know they were running."

Cole, as always, was convinced of the rotary's value. "No more big breakthroughs are needed," he stated, "before GM can produce usable rotary engines. If I weren't optimistic, I wouldn't be spending the corporation's money."

But the engine was still a very personal enterprise of his, and it seemed that GM aimed to introduce it to provide a sort of farewell present to Cole, due to retire at the same time as Gerstenberg at the end of 1974. The numbers to be produced during the 1975 model year (which runs from August 1974 to July 1975) were consistently increased, from a mere 30,000 to 100,000 then up to 165,000, though even this figure was, in GM's terms, consistent with the August 1972 statement about "limited production."

The shape of the engine also became clearer. GM was getting closer and closer to the Mazda idea, with variations. Gone were the simple ideas of 1970—the cast iron rotor housing, the absence of an oil cooler, and the single spark plug. These were replaced by an aluminum housing, a separate oil cooler, and two spark plugs. There would clearly be a number of improvements. The seals would be made of a new secret material; there would be a new carburetor developed by GM's own Rochester division and an ingenious device called EFE (early fuel evaporation), a "hot spot" of thin, easily heated metal between inlet and exhaust manifolds, designed to ensure that the engine would warm up even more quickly than the Wankel norm, already faster than that for a reciprocating engine. (Emissions are at their worst while an engine warms up.)

The number of cars into which a rotary engine might be put multiplied. A mini-Cadillac was much talked about—"mini" in a strictly relative sense, since the proposed vehicle was supposed to compete with the Mercedes models which had wrought such havoc in the luxury market in the early 1970s. Other candidates for the rotary were Firebirds and Camaros, besides the sportier version of the Vega that would be the first GM rotary. To stir up curiosity even further, GM exhibited two futuristic rotary cars at the Frankfurt, Paris, and London Motor Shows in the fall of 1973. These were possible future Corvettes, one with two, the other with four rotors tucked away behind the driver. Neat and compact, with low, simple lines, these prototypes were, to some Wankel enthusiasts, the first vehicles ever made which took full advantage of the engine's small size.

What emerged from the welter of rumors was the basic GM idea of producing a family of engines, on the same assembly lines, to power everything from the small Vivas and Kadetts made by GM's European subsidiaries up to at least its intermediate lines, leaving only the biggest models without rotaries.

The apparent scale of GM's plans set off a guessing game of trying to forecast the impact of the rotary on the whole car market. For the first time in the engine's history, quite reputable, sober, and independent forecasters were prepared to admit that the engine had a major future.

The most optimistic forecast naturally came from a rather biased source, *Ward's Wankel Report (WWR)*. This biweekly newsletter, started in July 1972, was an offshoot of one of the auto industry's standard sources of information, *Ward's Auto World*. WWR predicted that by 1980 the Wankel would have over half the U.S. car market. Ward estimated this at a mere 13 million units, not much more than a million above the 1973 figure. Even before the oil crisis of October 1973, Ward foresaw a slump in 1974, continuing into 1975. The 1973 sales figures would not be exceeded until 1977. Nevertheless, the forecasts were exceedingly ambitious: By 1980 GM would be selling 3.5 million rotary cars, out of a total production of 5.7 million vehicles. According to Ward's estimate, Ford would produce 1.5 million rotaries out of a total of 3 million vehicles. Even those two anti-Wankel stalwarts, Volkswagen and Chrysler, were due to sell 300,000 rotary vehicles apiece.

By contrast, the Eaton Corporation, a big and well-respected component supplier, issued a forecast (much quoted by Ford) which was more pessimistic. The future of the rotary, whose development "was equivalent to the 1930 piston engine," was limited by its high cost. Eaton seized on a point made by Yamamoto of Toyo Kogyo that despite its apparent simplicity, the rotary had problems of "technological density"—because it involved expensive materials and large numbers of fiddly bits making up the sealing system. Eaton compared five different types of engines on ten different grounds (noise, weight, emissions, durability, etc.), and its forecasts were consequently more soundly based than Ward's. It gave a "maximum possible" figure of forty percent of the market for rotaries in 1980. Its "probable range" of penetration was only from five to fifteen percent of the market. Yet even taking the Eaton Corporation's most pessimistic prediction, five percent, meant an annual production in the United States alone of well over half a million rotary vehicles, which would exceed the total number produced worldwide by 1973.

21

The Hangover

"The rotary engine will appeal only to the two percent of the
U.S. auto market that values novelty above all other features."
—Alan Loofbourrow of Chrysler

By the spring of 1973, a counterattack was being mounted on the
rotary. The first weapon was an alternative solution to the emissions
problem—the "stratified-charge" engine. This is based on the simple
scientific fact that you need a richer mixture to light a flame in a
combustion chamber than you do to keep one going. So why not
ensure cleaner and more complete combustion by "stratifying"—
layering or separating—the "charge" or input of gas and air to take
advantage of this phenomenon? Reciprocating engines breathe a
fairly uniform mixture of gas and air, but it is possible to separate
"rich" and "lean" mixtures in connected but separate chambers. The
late Sir Harry Ricardo had used the principle in developing a dual-
chamber diesel engine before World War II. Ford had been working
on its own PROCO system for stratification for some time.

But it took that Japanese genius Sochiro Honda to come up with
the most promising solution. Honda (like Henry Ford I) has always
retained an almost childlike attitude toward motors and, indeed,
business in general. He has never, for instance, worried about the
enormous loans extended toward his company by the mighty Mitsubishi Bank, for, as he said, "Am I not one of their best customers?"

Honda simply refused to admit that to satisfy the new emission
controls regulations, inelegant bolt-on contraptions were required.
"Stratified charge" was his alternative, and by 1971 he had succeeded in developing it. His system (like Ricardo's) used a separate

antechamber in which a rich gas-air mixture set off, like a detonator or primer, the leaner mixture in the main combustion chamber.

Henry Ford took to this idea—and to Honda personally—and talks began between Ford and Honda about a license. The system promised to meet any likely emission requirements without the need for the sort of gadgets favored by Cole and GM.

Ford, and another enthusiastic supporter of the stratified charge systems developed by Honda, the Texaco Oil Company, did not apparently realize that the Wankel's combustion system was naturally suited for stratified charge. (Ed Cole understood the point perfectly; in 1973 he filed a patent under his own name for a design using stratified charge in a rotary engine.)

In a Wankel, a continuous stream of air is moving faster than the flame lit by the spark plug. It is therefore possible to retain the stratification right through the combustion process in one rotary chamber since the mixture of gas and air does not get swirled and mixed up in the combustion chamber as it does in a reciprocating engine. What is usually a disadvantage for the Wankel now becomes a decided asset.

In theory, you have only to install a fuel injector, time the squirts of fuel to ensure a succession of rich-lean mixtures, and let the flow of the air and the shape of the chamber carry out the stratification. By contrast, in a reciprocating engine, even Ricardo and Honda had to resort to complicated second chambers to achieve the same result. Altering the shape of the hollow chamber on the side of the rotor where combustion takes place—normally a simple paddle shape but capable of hundreds of different variations without too much difficulty—will make stratification even more efficient.

As early as 1962, Max Bentele and Charles Jones at Curtiss-Wright had built at least two stratified-charge engines. Charles Jones has demonstrated a stratified-charge version of his standard RC 2-60 engine, which gives better fuel consumption and emissions at the relatively low speed of 2,000 rpm than the best reciprocating units. So Ford's championing of the stratified-charge idea as a weapon against the Wankel could prove to be a boomerang in the long run. His own engineers, in fact, worked so successfully on stratified-charge rotaries that they built one engine whose fuel consumption was comparable with an equivalent reciprocating unit. They even "showed Curtiss-Wright some stratified stuff that really shook them up," said one Ford engineer.

But the most important attacks on the rotary in 1973 were not based on the existence of an alternative solution to the emission problems. Instead, there were direct assaults on the Mazda, first on its reliability and maintenance problems, then on its fuel consumption. The basic texts for the first charge were two surveys carried out among several hundred Mazda owners by the Los Angeles market research firm of J. D. Power, whose independence was established by providing evidence for both sides of the argument.

Power's first survey, in 1972, was confined to the R-100, the only rotary then being sold in any quantity; the second included the RX-2, by then a well-used model. The majority of Mazda owners were enthusiastic. Nine out of ten would "definitely or probably recommend their rotary model to a friend." They warmly appreciated its "power, performance, . . . quietness, smoothness, acceleration," etc., and the approval figures for the RX-2 were better than for the R-100. But even the "earlier R-100 engine ratings were themselves significantly higher than usual among small car owners."

If the rotary was well loved, it was, nevertheless, an idiosyncratic machine, suitable only for an enthusiastic minority of drivers. According to one expert, "The mainstream of U.S. drivers do not know how to handle this engine as it is presently designed. In some respects, it needs much more care and attention to maintain than the average six- or eight-cylinder piston engine." Drivers were especially worried about the need to add oil every thousand miles or less and the shorter life of the spark plugs, but many probably ignored both these rotary peculiarities.

All these problems were "too much for the average American car driver to tolerate." And there was one specific problem: seals—not the apex or side seals, but the O-ring around the main engine shaft, designed to prevent the cooling oil from seeping through. These were originally made of rubber, and in the R-100 unit a significant number failed. The Power survey found that over a quarter of the cars surveyed that had done over 30,000 miles had failed in some way (though *Road Test* magazine found that one R-100 engine it stripped down was still sound after 85,000 miles on the road). Mazda spotted the fault, changed the O-ring on new cars to Teflon, a more reliable plastic material, and offered to replace any damaged rubber O-rings free.

The second Power survey had said that "the car driving public will also have to contribute in terms of learning effort and greater involvement in auto maintenance." Scarcely a practical possibility if the rotary was to make any sort of real progress. For the majority of garage mechanics were not properly trained in the repair of the rotary, and Mazda's policy was that there was "no such thing as a reconditioning of any of the major parts of a Mazda engine." Everything had to be replaced—even the simple iron side housings, which could be reconditioned for a quarter of the cost of a new part. The result was, as one expert said, "the standard of workmanship in [Mazda] dealers' yards is backyard in general and criminal at worst." After introducing the NSU Spyder, the first rotary-engined car sold in the United States, distributor Fred Oppenheimer had said flatly, "It is really a question of putting Swiss watchmakers into gas stations." It was probably more a question of getting used to a very new piece of machinery. Certainly, Mazda's dealers in Seattle, its first market, solved the problem simply enough by organizing a joint repair workshop.

The drivers in Power's survey were least happy with their cars' fuel consumption. Most of them rated it as only "fair." A third of the RX-2 owners claimed that they were getting 15 miles per gallon (mpg) or less when driving within city limits, and the median level for city driving was only 17.3 mpg. But Mazda buyers were still more worried about oil consumption.

Nevertheless, during the year—even before the sudden jump in gas prices as a result of the autumn oil crisis—the engine's thirst for gas had become a major disadvantage. A report in April 1973 from the federal government's Environmental Protection Agency (EPA) started the scare. Ironically, this should have been a triumph for the Mazda. For it confirmed the company's firm belief that, unlike any piston engine in production, the rotary could meet the EPA's 1975 pollution limits. But the EPA added that it had tested the rotary for fuel consumption and had found that it would give under eleven miles per gallon—the same as a big Buick sedan, in city driving conditions.

The EPA's test was controversial. It did not consist of an actual road test but a session on a test bed, a "rolling dynamometer" programmed to resemble the driving conditions met during a 7.5-mile drive in downtown Los Angeles—and from a cold start at that. Clearly these were conditions under which the Mazda was at its greatest disadvantage, and Brown reacted furiously to them. So did the specialist motor magazines. They ran their own test programs and found that in driving conditions more typical than those in the EPA's test cycle, the Mazda would do up to twenty miles per gallon. Nevertheless, these figures were below those of comparable cars, and they were confirmed from an apparently unimpeachable source. In the autumn, John Z. De Lorean, who had been in charge of the rotary program as head of Chevrolet, left GM. This was ominous for the Wankel—associated as it was with a trend to smaller vehicles. He had, apparently, wanted a greater emphasis placed on small cars than the top brass thought was desirable. But after his departure, De Lorean confirmed that the engine in its present state would use fifteen to twenty percent more fuel, depending on the type of driving involved, than a comparable reciprocating engine.

Even though gas prices had not yet started to move up, Mazda sales started to slide from the moment the EPA issued its horrifying figures—a trend helped by the wide publicity given to them. For a time the slide was masked because Mazda was in the middle of a major expansion of its sales outlets. Before a real counterattack could be launched against the notion of the rotary as a thirsty gas-guzzler, the October War and the jump in oil prices started to have its effect.

At first, ironically, sales of the notoriously gas-guzzling Mazda spurted with those of all other imports because the price of gas became a major factor for Americans deciding what type of car to buy, and foreign cars were associated with fuel economy. But the spurt did not last. Japanese prices had by now firmly overtaken American ones. Mazda rotaries had never been cheap; now they seemed positively expensive. The lowest price for Mazda's new, larger, and most luxurious vehicle, the RX-4, was over $4,000, and the cheapest rotary Mazda was only a few dollars under $3,500. All the Mazdas showed rises of at least ten percent on their 1974 prices compared with 1973. Despite the EPA, Brown had virtually hit the published 1973 sales target of 120,000 vehicles (helped by some judicious dealer rebates), but his dream of selling 300,000 vehicles by 1975 would have to remain just that.

In the early months of 1974, Mazda became just another car;

sales were down by two-fifths, more than for most imports, and Brown had to introduce a relatively cheap family sedan with reciprocating engine to help Mazda's dealers.

The EPA had driven further nails in the Mazda coffin by testing all 1974 models on the dynamometer and coming out, in late 1973, with a figure similar to those it had revealed in April 1973. Stung by the damage—Dick Brown estimated that the EPA had cost Mazda $100 million in lost sales—the company demanded a rerun, on a more typical driving cycle. This was duly granted and produced expected results—confirming that the Mazda could get up to twenty miles per gallon in normal driving conditions, but that its consumption was indeed above its competitors'. Brown fought back desperately, advising his dealers in January to

emphasize the fact that even our largest cars all fall within the top twenty-five percentile in terms of fuel economy by using the independent test material which we have previously sent to you. If you do get a complaint about fuel economy from an owner, make sure you take immediate steps to get the car in and checked out. The only time an owner should have a problem with fuel economy is if the car is abused, not properly tuned, or because of poor driving habits. An owner with a corrected complaint could turn out to be your best salesman.

By this time, the argument had become increasingly personal: Brown versus Eric Stork, the EPA administrator (who himself was fighting on two fronts: Because of the admitted fallibility of his, the EPA's, original test cycle, other federal agencies were gunning for the job of testing for pollution and mileage). In the end, Brown lost. His employers, used to a Japanese situation where businessmen rarely argue publicly with government agencies, eased him out in June 1974 after a squad of Japanese marketing men had been sent over to overhaul Mazda Motors of America.

Mazda's problems were not solved by some much improved 1974 cars and engines (the very ones whose prospects the EPA had so damaged). The newly introduced RX-4 answered most of the criticisms made of previous models. It was even better finished, even faster. The British magazine *Autocar* found that, unlike earlier models, which had been so sluggish at below 2,500 rpm, the RX-4 "will pull strongly from less than 1,000 rpm in either third or top gear." Elsewhere it was hailed as

by far the best piece of machinery they have come out with so far ... everything is so quiet and smooth you almost get mesmerized into thinking you are standing still and the rest of the world is moving by ... the basic interior materials ... avoid that "plastic city" mood too prevalent in many other Japanese cars today. ...

At the same time, Mazda made drastic changes to all its engines —those in the RX-2 and RX-3 as well as the RX-4. Most importantly, the old established single-piece carbon-aluminum seals, the first in rotary history to prove at all durable, were replaced by hard iron ones with a triangular corner piece, similar to those devised over a decade before by Bentele and Jones at Curtiss-Wright. What is more—the new seals were half the thickness of the old ones, a major step in reducing gas leakage and thus improving combustion efficiency. The side seals were single instead of double, and the shape of the combustion cavity in the side of the rotor was drastically altered—instead of a shallow scoop shape, the new hollow was deep and shaped like an old-fashioned bathtub. The rotor also had a new type of lining material, which the company refused to discuss.

Toyo Kogyo was, inevitably, the licensee worst affected by the oil crisis. Within a couple of months, the company could not find enough fuel oil for the fleet of car-carrying ships of which it was normally so proud, and as a result the whole area around the factory was double and triple parked with cars which it was unable to ship or for which it could not find a market. In the United States, too, its stocks mounted to 50,000 cars in the autumn of 1974, nearly enough to supply the U.S. market for a year at the much reduced level to which sales had dropped.

So the crisis ended Toyo Kogyo's hopes that thanks to the U.S. market it could manufacture rotary units in the numbers required to make, finally, some profit from its commitment to the engine. Even before it had to cut back production, Toyo Kogyo was producing only 20,000 rotary engines a month, under a third of the level it required for production to be really profitable.

At the same time, Toyo Kogyo was forced to surrender much of its independence to the Sumitomo Bank, on which it increasingly had to rely for financing. Indeed, it increasingly looked as if the company would share the fate of NSU, the other rotary pioneer, and fall into the hands of another company, in this case Toyota, which had been expected to take it over several years before.

Elsewhere, especially in the United States, the increased price of oil left the engine with few defenders. It was left to Felix Wankel himself to assert that his engine's alleged thirst was merely an excuse, not a real reason, for the enmity it aroused; if the Americans were so interested in petrol consumption, why, he asked, had they not taken to manufacturing the economical diesel in large numbers? But his was a lone voice. It was generally agreed that a time when car sales were slumping by a quarter or more (as they were after the October War) was no time for experimental engines of any sort. Detroit opted for short-term solutions, mostly involving a massive increase in the capacity to build smaller cars and engines of already proven design. The Wankel was not the only sufferer; in the first six months of the crisis, Ford and British Leyland both abandoned their efforts to produce a gas-turbine truck, and Ford and GM both stopped work on other long-term projects.

In this climate it is surprising that the Wankel survived at all. Henry Ford, never keen on the rotary, had already started to run down its prospects before the EPA tests. His attitude was blunt: He was against the rotaries "because they're no good; I don't like them."

He is alleged to have said that his company would not "produce them while I'm around." By the end of 1973, he was saying, "The Wankel is still on the X list around the Ford Motor Company . . . X means out, cross it out. We have an engineering group working on it, but I think the chances are that we will probably can that sometime in the near future." Suiting his action to his words, Ford let his secret option on a full Wankel license lapse at the end of the year—although the fact that Curtiss-Wright was worried about granting another GM-type license did not help the rotary cause. Early in March 1974, his company suspended work on the engine altogether, to the accompaniment of heavy hints from his disappointed engineers about the progress they had made and how the reasons for abandoning the program were not entirely concerned with the intrinsic merits of the rotary. (Nevertheless, Ford himself was adamant that the $5 to $10

million his company had spent on the rotary was money entirely
wasted.)

GM, of course, had spent too much to behave in the same cavalier
fashion as Ford. On the day before Christmas Eve 1973, GM announced that it would pay the fourth installment of its license fee,
but in a discreet final paragraph, issued at a time and in a form
designed to be overlooked, came a bombshell. The rotary-engined
Vega would not be introduced with the rest of the 1975 cars, but
would instead "probably" be introduced "sometime during the 1975
model year." Despite the festive season, the *Wall Street Journal*
picked up the story. And by the New Year, Detroit was ready to join
Henry Ford in running down the engine. All Cole's errors were
remembered: the Corvair (with its air-cooled aluminum unit, to his
enemies yet another Cole gimmick which had to be abandoned); the
air bag, a safety gimmick which he alone tried to promote. There
were even rumors that he was to be retired in disgrace in February,
six months before the due date.

The truth was more prosaic. The GM schedule was always ar-
rogantly tight, as were the design targets which Templin and his
successor had to meet. During the summer of 1973, before the oil
crisis, the tightness caught up with the program—as early as July,
David Cole was advising his father to postpone the introduction of
the engine for a few months. GM had set a strict fuel consumption
target—the rotary-engined Vega should be "comparable" with the
six-cylinder unit already installed. To get the necessary seventeen to
twenty miles per gallon, GM had moved the two spark plugs on each
rotor further apart. The move set up new stresses around the inlet
ports, which caused cracking. Yet more redesign proved necessary
—a new scraper seal designed by Toyo Kogyo had, for instance, to be
introduced. At the same time, the production lines at Hydra-Matic
were "just a hole in the ground" only a few months before the
original target production date. But, despite waves of rumors to the
contrary, the program was not killed off during the grim early days of
1974 when, for the first time since World War II, GM's sales slumped
more than the average for the industry; for once GM's strength in
bigger, more expensive vehicles, formerly a major asset in making it
the most profitable car maker in the world, became a liability as tens
of thousands of workers were laid off.

Even if GM did not kill the rotary program, it was, inevitably, severely pruned. The ambitious plans for replacing so many orthodox units, for whole new generations of low-slung, compact yet roomy rotary-engined vehicles, were chopped out in favor of a much more modest program. The rotary would be merely one engine option in a new, sporty Vega derivative, which would also be sold with a new and extremely compact V-8 and a four-cylinder engine —the only real effect of the rotary on its design was that the car would be lower slung, with a lower bonnet line than was possible with a normal-sized engine.

Worse was to come. At the end of September, in one of his last statements as president of GM before his retirement, Cole admitted that the corporation was indefinitely postponing production of the rotary. The ostensible reason was that none of the rotary engines it was likely to produce in the foreseeable future could cope with the federal antipollution standards being proposed for the 1977 model year, and GM did not want to be caught producing a rotary car for only a few months before it had to be withdrawn from the market before the end of 1976.

The move was partly political: GM, like the other major auto makers, was anxious to find some way of protesting at what they regarded as increasingly unreasonable demands. (A recent report by the National Academy of Sciences had admitted that antipollution standards were already higher than strictly necessary.) But GM's technical reasoning was also impressive.

It was spelled out late in October, in a letter to Senator Muskie from Cole's successor, Elliott M. ("Pete") Estes. For the first time since GM had taken out a rotary license, nearly four long years before, the corporation revealed just how far it had got in developing the engine. And, although the letter was designed to show the impracticality of rotary production in the immediate future, it made comparatively cheering reading for rotary enthusiasts.

The engine was indeed dirty (four times as much hydrocarbon as an orthodox unit and, surprisingly, just as much oxides of nitrogen); although it was comparatively easy to bring down the pollution levels on a new engine to percentages small enough to comply with the 1975 standards, the efficiency of the catalytic converter would almost certainly decline by a quarter during the 50,000-mile assumed life of the engine; and this "system deterioration" made the rotary a doubtful proposition even for the 1975 standards because the converter had so much more work to do than on an orthodox engine. And the rotary could only—just—reach the proposed 1977 levels by the use of both a thermal reactor and a catalytic converter and then only on a new engine.

But the report also destroyed the idea that the rotary was inevitably a "gas-guzzler." One of its tables compared the GMRE with two orthodox engines, one a six-cylinder, the other a V-8. According to the EPA tests, the rotary was under a tenth more thirsty than either of the other engines. On GM's own "suburban" test, it gave marginally *better* consumption than the competition, yet the performance from zero to sixty miles per hour was substantially better than the six-cylinder engine's, and marginally better than the V-8's.

Finally, Estes emphasized that the rotary program was being postponed, emphatically not canceled, and that GM looked "forward to the future possibility of being able to offer the engine to our customers." The letter worked. In early 1975 the pollution standards due in 1977 were indefinitely postponed in the interests of fuel economy, as Estes had obviously hoped. This decision gave GM the choice of going ahead with the Wankel in a number of ways. It could refine the present design to ensure that it conformed with the 1975 standards right through the 50,000-mile cycle (not a major task). Or it could wait for the "second-generation" engines now known to be under development. One would be a stratified-charge version of the present unit; another would be an entirely new engine, smaller than the present GMRE, but much faster running at up to 12,000 rpm, possibly twice the cruising speed of the present rotary; a third would be a much larger engine, exploiting to the full the rotary's increasing advantages of compactness and lightness as the power of the engine increased.

The situation was further confused when GM delayed the penultimate license payment due just before Christmas 1974 while it renegotiated the whole agreement with NSU and Curtiss-Wright. The revised agreement was not finally announced until early February 1975, and provided for a respite for GM—which by then was minus $12.35 million in 1974 and $6.175 million in 1975.°

GM negotiated two alternative arrangements to give it time to make up its mind about future Wankel policy. Either way $3 million

° The original agreement provided for the payments to be of $10 million and $5 million respectively, but successive revaluations of the Deutschemark had greatly increased the dollars to be paid to NSU, recipient of 6/11ths of the royalties from the GM license.

was to be paid in June 1975, then, in June 1976, it could either pay a final $12 million, or a continuing royalty of $5 an engine. Clearly, if by then GM has decided to go ahead with any form of mass production, it will prefer the lump sum payment.

But, in Cole's absence, GM's future plans are highly uncertain. It is unlikely to scrap the rotary altogether after investing at least $150 million in it; it could, however, justify Henry Ford's prophecy that GM would "merely make 100,000 as a power option. If they sell it at a $600 premium, they might get their money back."

Against the rotary is one personal point—Estes was the executive who succeeded Cole at Chevrolet and stopped production of Cole's pet Corvair, and, clearly, any such revolutionary idea requires considerable personal backing. But the precedent of the automatic transmission is encouraging. Ralph Cross, chairman of the leading machinery manufacturers of the same name, told *Ward's Wankel Report* in late 1973 that the rotary "reminds me of the first automatic transmission made by Buick in the early 1950s. There were all kinds of field problems, and finally Buick threw up its hands. The automatic transmission might have died right there if it hadn't been for Alfred Sloan, GM's president at the time. He started all over again by setting up the Detroit Transmission Division. It's now GM's Hydra-Matic Division. . . . Sloan had guts," he added, "and Ed Cole's showing the same faith and courage with the GMRE Vega. It's too bad he's retiring just when it's coming to market."

In fact, Cole retired before the rotary came to market. But even if GM never produces a rotary-engined car or produces one in comparatively small numbers to get a token return on its investment, as Ford suggests, its decision will not be fatal for the rotary's prospects (though David Cole, for one, believes otherwise; he told me that only GM and Ford had the necessary resources to carry through the rotary revolution). Yet although GM produced only a token number of one model of car—the Oldsmobile Toronado—with front-wheel drive, this earlier technical advance, like the Wankel, space-saving, advanced, and initially expensive, is still gaining ground, even among formerly hostile American-owned auto manufacturers.

Indeed, the rosy long-term future for the rotary was the single most striking aspect of a November 1974 report undertaken for the U.S. government by the Rand Corporation. To Rand, a turbocharged, stratified-charge Wankel made considerable sense as the long-term answer to shortages of fuel and materials.

But this was virtually the only good news for the rotary throughout 1974. The rotary-engined Citroen GS proved a commercial flop, and in the autumn Comotor, faced with a stockpile of engines adequate for a couple of years' sales, temporarily stopped production of rotary engines. So until VW launches its expected rotary-engined vehicle in 1976, and until GM takes the plunge, this leaves only the struggling Toyo Kogyo making rotary-engined cars. And for Toyo Kogyo as well, 1976 could easily be the next rotary boom year. By that time it will have cleared its immense backlog of unsold cars and be marketing newer models—a rumored smaller RX-5, and, above all, engines which will, thanks to stratified charge and improved ignition, actually use less fuel than comparable orthodox units. (Yamamoto has firmly stated that TK's existing engines can cope with even the presently foreseeable level of 1977 emission standards, still without using a catalytic converter.)

Even before that date, however, the great boost given by GM to the rotary scene will be bearing indirect fruit. A number of rotary-engined motorcycles, conceived as a result of the great Wankel upsurge of 1971–72, were born in late 1974; Suzuki unveiled a machine with an engine based firmly (and admittedly) on a Mazda original; the German DKW produced a machine with a Fichtel and Sachs engine especially developed for motorcycle use; and a small Dutch manufacturer, Van-Veen of Amsterdam, employed a Comotor engine for its "superbike." All three were inevitably smoother than the competition.

For the rotary engine, and its proponents, are tenacious. They have survived numerous bankruptcies and takeovers; they have recovered the engine from the previous disasters. And each time some new force—be it Hurley's interest, or the GM license, or the Mazda boom—has propelled it forward, some of the progress remains even after the particular tide has receded.

(22)

Will the "Old Man" Ever Die?

"The rotary is like a twenty-five-year-old man full of promise.
The piston engine is an old man about to die."

—KENICHI YAMAMOTO

For an "old man" the piston engine is still proving remarkably spry and capable of feats of rejuvenation which continually confound its critics and make the task of any rival motor more difficult by the year. But rotary enthusiasts can point to the sailing ship and the steam locomotive which, spurred by the competition, reached their peak of efficiency just before they were finally supplanted by the steamship and the diesel-electric locomotive.

They can legitimately say that the rotary has had such a difficult birth, such a disturbed childhood, such an unruly adolescence, a band of such curious and often unhelpful supporters, that the mere fact of its survival is a major triumph. They can point to the allegedly insuperable barriers it has already surmounted. The engine has been condemned as dirty—only to become a white hope in the fight against pollution. The sealing system, that bugbear of the rotary throughout its history, would, it was thought, never be durable enough to satisfy the rigors of automotive use. Yet Comotor now says it has rotaries on test whose seals are so durable that the test benches crack up before the engine.

The latest "insuperable" barrier is the Wankel's thirst for increasingly expensive gasoline—as we saw, itself a trick question because the rotary would be content with much rougher fuel than is at present available. As the author writes, the verdict on the "thirst penalty" remains unproved. The author believes that the rotary diesel, stratified charge—or even a few more years of development on combustion systems—will prove this latest barrier to be as ephemeral as the others. Anyone who has ever worked on developing the engine insists on the speed of the rotary "learning curve," how dangerous it can be to freeze a design since tomorrow is so likely to bring a fresh batch of test results promising further advances in fuel economy, durability, producibility, or some other crucial point. Indeed, the certainty that better engines were on the way has been a major factor in delaying the introduction of General Motors' rotary unit.

The author is confident that the rotary engine will survive and flourish, if in unexpected areas—for example, in leisure vehicles where pollution pressures undermine the value of the two-stroke engine. In the words of Yura Arkus Duntov, it took an "unlikely combination of a small German motorcycle manufacturer and an American aircraft company" to develop the idea into a reality, and the only predictable element in the engine's future uses—and users—is their unpredictability.

The only two boards of directors that have taken the decision to develop the Wankel on logical and commercial grounds, the German Fichtel and Sachs and the American Outboard Marine, are both largely in the two-stroke business. Companies in the motor industry—not to mention Curtiss-Wright—all took up the Wankel challenge partly, or largely, for irrational reasons, imagination, vision, or megalomania, depending on your viewpoint, in the chief executive. Without Tsuneji Matsuda, Toyo Kogyo would never have taken out a license; nor would have General Motors without Ed Cole, nor Citroen without Bercot, nor NSU without the trio of enthusiastic engineers running the show.

The opposition has had another psychological aspect. It was perfectly reasonable for companies like Fiat, British Leyland, or Renault, principally manufacturers of small vehicles, to turn down the rotary idea as unsuitable, often after tests more thorough than they ever admit in public. However, there was a personal element in the decision of Henry Ford and his company (and possibly Daimler-Benz as well) not to go ahead with production of the rotary, which is so entirely suitable for the size of vehicles they produce, even after their design and development efforts had been more successful than those of some of the engine's producers. The aggressive hostility of Chrysler—and so much of the American press—is also puzzling and inexplicable on purely logical grounds.

But the irrational nature of so much of the support for the engine has had its disadvantages. The idea of a rotary engine became the personal property of a number of chief executives, and thus tied it to the fate of a group of men who were inevitably accident-prone precisely because of the qualities that had led them to take up the Wankel in the first place.

But this is not a story likely to satisfy those who like logical explanations. The rotary was not totally neglected—as it ought to have been if big business is as implacably closed to new ideas as some would make out. The Wankel story also contradicts the thesis that the business world is now the exclusive preserve of giant companies dominated by committees of faceless men.

Those who look for a juicy conspiracy or two to liven up their view of business history will find some, but these turn out either to be relatively innocent, like IBB's involvement, or ineffectual, like Max Bunford's dream of a truly European motor company. Those who want virtue always to be rewarded—or inevitably punished—will be equally dumbfounded. Wankel, rightly, made his fortune. But Lindenmayr, Bentele, Hurley, Bensinger, Dick Brown, who all contributed greatly to turning Wankel's dream into reality, acquired less kudos—not to mention hard cash—out of the engine than the controversial Ernst Hutzenlaub or Hurley's successors at Curtiss-Wright.

Certainly the story of the Wankel engine should dispel any illusion that companies are motivated purely by the profit motive. For myself, this is the most comforting lesson to be learned from the story: Many business decisions are taken for reasons that are personal before they are economic, to be explained by the psychologist rather than the financial analyst or the student of business theory—and thank God for it.

Sources

The library of books on the Wankel engine is small and, for the layman, disconcertingly technical. By far the most interesting is Jan Norbye's *The Wankel Engine* (Chilton Books, New York), a mine of information, personal as well as technical. Felix Wankel's own book, *Rotary Piston Machines* (Iliffe Books, London), is fascinating chiefly because of the elaborate categories of rotary machines so profusely illustrated at the back and also because the immense effort revealed in the book is a living reproof to those who would belittle Wankel's contribution to the rotary art. The book by Wankel's translator Richard Ansdale, *The Wankel RC Engine* (Iliffe), I frankly found incomprehensible. Far better as a student's textbook is the work by the great Japanese engineer, Kenichi Yamamoto (published by his employer, Toyo Kogyo).

Even more useful than these books have been the *Ward's Wankel Reports*, published since July 1972 by Ward's Communications, Inc., 28 West Adams Street, Detroit, Michigan. And from the mass of journalism—technical, financial, and general—on the subject, the contributions of Karl Ludvigsen, including his rotary dictionary, *Wankel A to Z*, which he published himself, stand out like a beacon through the mists.

Index

KM3, the, 158–59
KM37, the, 156–58
Klein, Stefan, 119, 120, 122, 125
Klockner-Humboldt-Deutz, 141
Koppgrinder, the, 189
Korean War, the, 31, 60, 61
Korp, Dieter, 36
Kovacik, Bob, 199
Kreiskolbenmotor, *see* KKM
Krupp, 141
Kugelfischer company, 61–62

Lahr, 17
Lamm, Dr., 97–98
lawn mowers, 66, 159, 182
Le diverse e artificiose macchine del Capitane Agostino Ramelli, 20–21
Leiding, Rudolf, 114, 115, 116
Levitt, William J., 149, 150
licensing arrangements for Wankel engines, 81–84
Lindau, 16, 27, 29, 33, 35, 96
Lindenmayr, Peter, 55, 56, 57, 58, 63, 64, 169, 188
London and Rhodesian Estates, *see* Lonrho
Lonrho, 117–27, 147
Loofburrow, Alan G., 207, 223
Lotz, Kurt, 108, 110, 113, 114, 115
Ludvigsen, Karl, 49, 50, 56, 72, 151, 154, 181
Luftwaffe, the, 29
Lundqvist, Karl, 55
lurching motion, in rotary engines, 39, 40, 45, 46

machinery, for production of rotary engines, 40
Mahle company, 98
Maillard, Bernard, 54
MAN company, 141
Massey-Ferguson group, 141
Matsuda, Kohei, 129, 210, 211
Matsuda, Tsuneji, 128, 237
Mazda, 79, 129, 134
 rotary, 135, 137, 138, 181–82, 192–99

Mazda Motors of America (MMA), 195–96
Mazer, Joseph, 206
Mercedes-Benz cars, 17, 118
Mercedes company, 96, 99
Metco, 161
Methanol, 44
Michelin family, 102
Michelotti, 77
Miron, Elihu, 111, 112, 114
Mitsubishi group, 211
Model Roland, 201, 202
Mohr, Jim, 159
Mopeds, 32
Morgan Guaranty Trust, 170
Morganite, 91
Morihawa, Jiro, 196
motorcycles, 25, 26, 32, 33, 40–42, 76, 90, 92, 105, 132, 209, 235
motor racing, 49
Mundy, Harry, 96
Munich, 61, 78
Munich Patent Office, 54
Munich Symposium 1960, 152
Murdoch, William, 21
Murphy, Thomas A., 186
My Years With General Motors, 165

Nader, Ralph, 167, 183
Nairobi, 119
Nallinger, Professor Friedrich, 58, 73, 78
National Academy of Sciences, 232
Nazi Party, 26, 27
Neckarsulm, 115
Neckarsulm Strickmachinen Union, *see* NSU
New Yorker, 151
New York Society of Investment Analysts, 202
New York Times, 193–94
Nibel, Dr. Otto, 27
Nicasil alloy, 98
Nigeria, 118
Nissan company, 82, 130, 138, 192, 210, 214–15
nitrogen, oxides of (NO_x), 171